Science and Technology

for the Early Years

Purposeful Play Activities

Pauline Allen

 **Brilliant Publications**

Published by Brilliant Publications, 1 Church View, Sparrow Hall Farm, Edlesborough, Dunstable, Bedfordshire LU6 2ES, United Kingdom

Tel: 01525 229720
Fax: 01525 229725
E-mail: sales@brilliantpublications.co.uk
Website: www.brilliantpublications.co.uk

Written by Pauline Allen
Illustrated by Lynda Murray
Cover designed and illustrated by Lynda Murray

Printed in Malta by Interprint Limited
First published in 2002, reprinted in 2003
10 9 8 7 6 5 4 3 2

Contents

Introduction

Young children encounter new experiences constantly and seek to understand them in order to extend their skills, develop their confidence and build upon their present knowledge and awareness.

The *Curriculum Guidance for the Foundation Stage* addresses the needs of children from the age of three years to the end of their time in the reception class of primary school. The *Early Learning Goals* establish expectations for most children to reach by the end of the foundation stage but are not a curriculum in themselves. The guidance includes stepping stones of progress, identifying developing knowledge, skills, understanding and attitudes that children need.

It is the responsibility of practitioners to plan a curriculum that will help children make good progress towards and, where appropriate, beyond the early learning goals.

Children learn through:

* playing, alone and with others
* talking to themselves, peers and adults
* observing, using all their senses
* planning what to say and do
* questioning everything that puzzles them

* experimenting with tools and materials
* testing out new ideas and actions
* repeating and practising thoughts and actions
* reflecting on experiences
* responding to new ideas and activities.

Well-planned play is a key way children learn with enjoyment and challenge during the foundation years, and children of all ages need to play and learn from their thoughts and actions.

Opportunities need to be provided for:

* child-initiated activities and adult-initiated activities

* children's own intentions and adult aims

* children's meanings and adult interpretations

* potential learning outcomes and planned learning outcomes

* individual needs and small/large group needs

* familiarity and security and challenge and risk

* spontaneity and flexibility and routine and structure.

The curriculum for the foundation stage should underpin all future learning by supporting, fostering, promoting and developing children's

* personal, social and emotional well-being
* positive attitudes and dispositions towards their learning
* social skills
* attention skills and persistence
* language and communication
* reading and writing
* mathematics
* knowledge and understanding of the world
* physical development
* creative development.

All of these contribute to a child's growing awareness of all things scientific and technological. The main focus is, however, through activities which develop *their knowledge and understanding of the world* and through the extension of their *creative abilities,* which enables them to explore and communicate their ideas.

Activities aimed at extending knowledge and understanding of the world provide opportunities to solve problems, make decisions, experiment, predict, plan and question in a range of varied contexts as well as to explore and find out about their environment and people and places that have significance in their lives.

Aspects of planned experiences for creative development provide opportunities for all children to explore and share their thoughts, ideas and feelings through a variety of art, design and technology, music, movement, dance and imaginative and role-play activities.

The following section contains ideas for designing resource areas to stimulate purposeful play. The lists for each of the areas will be useful for planning.

The remainder (and bulk) of the book contains planned activities which can be used to ensure that the children have a wide variety of new science, design and technology experiences.

Planned use of resource areas

At some point throughout the year children should have the opportunity to be introduced to the tools and equipment in each of the following areas. All skills need to be taught and much time needs to be given to the practice of the specific skills required in each of these learning areas:

* Book corner
* Sand tray
* Water play
* Scientific and mathematical equipment and artefacts
* Writing area
* Imaginative play area
* Creative media corner
* Construction kits and big toys
* Computer and concept keyboard station
* Food and cooking equipment area
* Plants, animals and materials around us
* Sounds and music
* Games and group activities.

The organization of the space and the use of the resources within that space can contribute to many areas of learning for the children. It is important that the aims and purpose of the activity are clear in order to create an appropriate focus for each activity.

Planning

The following pages can be used as a tool when planning activities that are aimed at developing the children's knowledge and understanding of the world and extending their creative skills. The suggestions can be marked and dated as they are used throughout the year, as a record or planning sheet (a space has been left beside each suggestion to enable you to insert a date). Where there is a direct link with an activity suggested in this book, the set and number are given. Extra activities and ideas can be added to the lists.

Each resource area is matched to the most appropriate early learning goals and to the nearest match in the science and technology programmes of study (National Curriculum 2000). This is to enable teachers to plan for continuity and progression with an easy transition from one stage to the next. It will also be of use to teachers in small schools who have both Reception and Year 1 children in their class.

Book corner

ELG K & U of the world, Creative development
NC   Sc1 Science enquiry, Research
DT Product information

* Story books (B10, C4, D2, D5, D8, D9, D10, E1, F5, G1, G2, G4, G6, H1, H5, H8, I10, K4, K10)
* Rhymes (A1, B7, C5, D2, E3, F1, H7, H10, I8, J1, J2, J4, J9, K4, K6)
* Poems (G5)
* Encyclopedia (B8, H8)
* Books to touch, scratch and feel (A7, E7)
* Picture books (B1, B9)
* Games books
* Mirror books (I9)
* Information books (A8, B2, B8, C9, D9, I6)
* Activity books
* Pop-up and flap books (K8)
* Dictionary (K4)
* Word play games (D6, D7)
* Interactive books and CD-Roms (B6, C2, L2)
* Science reference books (A8, B3, B6)
* Class books (C6, E8)
* Diaries (C3, C6)
* Photo albums (A8, H6)
* Big books
* Group readers
* Plays
* Pictures and charts (B1, B6, C2, D5, F7, H6, L1)
* Map books and atlases (D8)
* Guidebooks
* Leaflets
* Posters (G10)
* Newspapers
* Comics
* Catalogues (F3, H6, L1)
* Recipes (Set G)
*
*
*

Also use:
* special displays and collections about one area of interest
* on-going class books
* class books as a record of past activities
* books with accompanying tapes and CD-Roms
* books of different shapes and sizes (bought and made)
* books to take home
* books from home
* activity books with materials and apparatus
*
*
*

Sand tray

ELG K & U of the world, Creative development
NC   Sc2 Humans, Sc3 Natural materials

Change the focus of the activity each week:
* dry sand
* damp sand
* wet sand
* coarse or fine sand (silver sand or beach sand)
* pebbles – dry, damp and in water
* gravel – dry and wet
* compost
* sawdust
* clay – damp and very wet
* wheat (untreated) with toy tractors
* stones, including fossils
* pasta, various shapes and colours
*
*
*
*

Investigate:
* building, pouring, digging, and filling containers (E5)
* using dry, damp and wet materials; encourage children to experience the difference in feel, and how it can be used (E5)

* using sand tray as a base for creating model scenes, roadways and networks; add toy cars, diggers, farm or zoo animals, model houses or spaceships (A1, D5, D10)
* using spoons, spades, hands, containers, funnels, sieves, forks, shovels (E5)
* making timers and compare with manufactured sandtimers (E5)
* making prints and patterns with rakes, forks, hands, feet, etc (E5)
* writing messages (E5)
* hunting for buried treasure (E5)
* using shells, pebbles, seaweed, flags, buckets, sand moulds and spades (E5)
*
*
*
*

Water play

ELG K & U of the world, Creative development
NC   Sc2 Senses, Sc3 Materials, Sc4 Forces

Change the focus of the activity each week:
* clear water
* coloured water
* bubbles
* add baby oil
* add salt
* cold water
* warm water
* deep water
* shallow water
* outdoors – a tap or hosepipe, puddle or paddling pool
* washing up
* wash day
* investigate sinking/floating; find things that float on the surface, things that float under the surface, things that sink, things that gradually sink; make floating things sink, eg drinks can, plastic tray (E1)
* use things with holes that will sink and float (E3)
* find things to fill and pour; explore which containers hold the same amount of water (H7)
* use things water will move, eg waterwheel (E1)
* explore things that soak up water (sponges) – do they become heavy, change colour, hold much water? (E4)

* try squirting water (bottles, syringes, etc) making water pushers (E1)
* add ice cubes, watch how they float – do they melt quickly? Use warm and cold water (A9); make ice balloons (E1)
* use water toys and watch how they work (E1)
* try siphoning and using pipes and tubes, hosepipe and straws (E1)
*
*
*

Scientific and mathematical equipment and artefacts

ELG K & U of the world, Creative development
NC   Sc2 Living things, Sc3 Materials, Sc4 Forces, Light

* magnets (K7)
* blowing bubbles – variety of shapes of bubble blowers, sizes, coloured water (Set E)
* ice balloons (made by filling a balloon with water and freezing it) – variety of shapes, sizes, coloured water (E1)
* a new pet (Set B)
* toys – wind-up, gravity, push-and-pull, friction, battery-powered, etc (K3)
* colours – masks, spinners, acetates, colour sets, kaleidoscopes, sunglasses and shades (Set I)
* light – torches, mirrors, reflective surfaces, baubles, periscopes, optical viewers, transparent materials (Set I, Set L)
* air – bubbles, balloons, windmills, things to waft, musical instruments, things that fall slowly and quickly, inflatable toys, mobiles (D4, K2)
* ourselves – clothes, food, appearance, capability, parts of body, families, needs, health, homes, movements (Set A, K9, K10)
* texture and patterns of natural and manufactured objects (Set E)
* structures and shapes (Set F)
* torches, electricity kits (Set L)
* thermometers, stethoscopes (A8)
* hand lenses (B6, C8, D1)
*
*

Writing area

ELG K & U of the world, Creative development
NC   Sc3 Materials and their properties

* Set E: Exporing materials

Vary the range of papers and tools to 'mark', write, or record visually:

* variety of sizes and shapes of paper (I2)
* variety of colours and textures of paper (tissue, greaseproof, tracing, etc) (I2)
* collection of pencils, from 4H to 4B; different shapes for holding (D8, I1)
* collection of felt-tip pens (I1)
* variety of types of wax crayon (E8, I1)
* erasers and pencil sharpeners (D8)
* letters and envelopes of different sizes (F2)
* whiteboard and pens (I2)
* blackboard and chalks (I2)
* stamps and printing set (F2)
* charcoal pencils (I1)
* sticky labels (K4)
* special occasion cards and notelets (D8)
* picture postcards (D8)
*
*
*

Imaginative play area

ELG K & U of the world, Creative development
NC   Sc3 Materials and their properties

✳   Set H: Variety of materials
Investigate:
✳   choice of garments and textures, with a variety of
         fastenings (A8, F7)
✳   examples of indoor and outdoor wear (Set H)
✳   fabrics which stretch, fray, are waterproof, thin,
         flimsy (H2, H3)
✳   fabrics which show signs of 'wear and tear' (H2)
✳   fabrics made in a variety of ways, eg knitted,
         woven, crocheted (H3, H4)
✳   belts, sashes, ties, scarves, ribbons (safety
         aspect) (F7)
✳   transparent, translucent and opaque materials,
         decorative glitter and shine (I5, I8)
✳   animal masks/costumes
✳   finger, hand and string puppets (F5)
✳   glow-in-the-dark, reflective and luminous
         materials and clothes (I7, I8)
Ideas to develop:
✳   tea party (H7, H8)
✳   workshop/garage (F10, H9)
✳   teddy bears' picnic (H10)
✳   wash day (H1)

✳   hospital corner (A9)
✳   pet shop (B1)
✳   underwater world (D9)
✳   post office (F2)
✳   building site (F9)
✳   travel agent (D8)
✳   bus journey (K6)
✳
✳
✳
✳
✳
✳
✳

Creative media corner

ELG K & U of the world, Creative development
NC   Sc2 Senses, Sc3 Materials, Sc4 Colour, Light

✳   powder paint – investigate mixing, solutions, powders, consistencies (I1, I2)

✳   different applicators – wide and fine brushes, sponges, printing, blowing using straws, splatter pictures, bubble prints, spoons, eye-droppers, syringes (I1)

✳   different media – chalk, pastels, wax, felt-tip pens (large and small) (I1)

✳   modelling – Plasticine, playdough, air-drying clay, ordinary clay, papier mâché, pipe cleaners (B3, B9, D10, E9, H7, H8, K9)

✳   variety of surfaces – types of paper, card, plastic, tin-foil, etc. Try drawing, writing and painting on them (E8, G10)

✳   overlays of materials, transparent and coloured (I5)

✳   ways to cut, stick and join (make feely numbers and letters) (Set F)

✳   adding colour – face paints, dyes (I2)

✳   the effect of drying – paints, modelling materials (E5, H8)

✳   colour washes and special effects (I1)

✳   observational drawing (C2, C3)

✳   designing and making activities – using the most appropriate materials (A3)

✳   variety of wood and appropriate tools (safety aspect) (F4)

✳   found materials for modelling and joining (B7)

✳   decorative paper and card collection (E5)

✳   collages (B1, C5, E6, I10)

Construction kits and big toys

ELG K & U of the world, Creative development
NC Sc2 Ourselves, Sc3 Materials, Sc4 Forces

* use large bricks and construction kits; make Humpty Dumpty's wall and the three little pigs' houses (Set F)
* create structures that are strong and safe, eg tall towers to fly a flag, a climbing frame for an action character (F8)
* collage of textures and materials (Set E, I10)
* explore the movements of the body (A1, A6, K9)
* investigate the differences in pulling, pushing, sliding, lifting, holding, rolling, dropping; make something to push, pull or sail (K3, K4, K5, K9)
* create structures to use as a ramp to investigate moving vehicles; roll a car down a ramp to hit a target or knock over a skittle (K10)
* make models with moving parts, levers, hinges, lids, pop-up parts, springs, wheels and cogs – see-saw and slide for Teddy (F5, H9, K5, K8)
* make dens, towers and bridges (F9)
* large strong cardboard boxes (F9, K4)
* create a 3-D model of an area (B10, D5, D10, K1)
* make the bus to play 'The wheels on the bus' (K6)
* big toys (H9, K4)
*
*
*
*
*

Computer and concept keyboard station

ELG K & U of the world, Creative development
NC Sc1 Science enquiry skills

* concept keyboard familiarization skills – range of games (G10, L2)
* adventure games (L2)
* draw programs (I2, L2)
* early reading programs (J9, L2)
* CD-Roms to find pictures (D5, E7)
* My World program – *Dressing Teddy* (D8)
* tape-recorder (A4, G9, J7, J10, L2)
* videos (D5, F5, J5, J7, K1)
* CD-Rom research (B3, B6, B7, B8, B9, C2, E8)
* computer music program (J8)
* telephone skills (J9)
* programmable toys (L3)
*
*
*
*
*

Food and cooking equipment area

ELG K & U of the world, Creative development
NC   Sc2 Senses, Sc3 Materials

✳   Set G: Changing materials (food)
Investigate:
✳   diluting drinks (G8)
✳   making sandwiches (G1)
✳   ice lollies (E1)
✳   teddy bears' picnic (H10)
✳   food smells (A7)
✳   making jellies (G3)
✳   melting substances (G7)
✳   changes in state (Set G)
✳   flavours of crisps for senses – taste and smell
          tests (C9)
✳   dissolving (G9)
✳   milk products (B8)
✳   mixing food substances – flours, sugars, salt,
          water, oil, milk, vinegar, etc (G4, G5)
✳   packaging (G6)
✳   collecting examples of different ways of
          preserving (G6)

✳   favourite foods (G1)
✳   healthy eating (G1)
✳   baking materials and equipment (G2)
✳   foods around the world, festival foods (C10,
          G10)
✳   bird cake (B3)
✳
✳
✳
✳
✳
✳
✳

Plants, animals and materials around us

ELG K & U of the world, Creative development
NC Sc2 Plants, animals and environment,
     Sc3 Materials, Sc4 Forces and motion, Light

* Set B: Animals
* Set C: Plants, leaves and flowers
* Set D: Out of doors

Investigate:
* pets (B1)
* wild animals – wormery, aquarium (Set B)
* finding and making a variety of habitats for animals, eg make a spider's web with wool (B4, B5, B7, D9)
* pond study, wild area – natural habitats to explore (B6)
* variety of plants/seeds, skills of planting and growing (Set C, D7)
* growing tools: pots, trays, seeds, bulbs, plants (Set C)
* gardening – digging, weeding, planting, watering, etc (Set C)
* living, dried and artificial flowers (Set C)
* rocks and soils around the area (D1)
* weather study (D4)
* shadows of objects, buildings and people (L4)
* long-term changes in plants (C3, C4, C5, C6)
* the wider world (D5, D8)

* PE and movement/small PE apparatus, climbing and playground equipment – balance, movement, forces (A6, K5, K9, K10)
* playground games (K10)
* local traffic study (K1)
* balloons and bubbles, flags, streamers and banners – wind direction and force (D4, E2, K2)

Sounds and music

ELG K & U of the world, Creative development
NC   Sc2 Senses, Sc3 Materials, Sc4 Senses

✳   Set J: Sound
Investigate:
✳   making noises in time to music (Set J)
✳   making noises to create rhythms (Set J)
✳   singing songs (B10, Set J)
✳   action rhymes (A1, B7, J1, J2, J4, K6)
✳   making sounds with artefacts, making
          instruments (Set J)
✳   making sounds with computer keyboard (J8)
✳   recognizing taped sounds (A4, Set J)
✳   sound-recognition games (A4, J7)
✳   moving to sounds (J2, J4, J8)
✳   dance steps (J8)
✳   sounds in the home (J9, J10)
✳   alarm sounds (J9, J10)
✳   natural sounds (J10)
✳   making up stories to include sound effects (J10)
✳
✳
✳
✳

Games and group activities

ELG Language and literacy, K & U of the world
**   Creative development, Physical development**

✳   Simon says (K9)
✳   snap and matching games (A7, D6, D7, H2, H3,
          H6, J7, J10)
✳   puppets (A1, F5)
✳   sorting games (B10, E10, H5)
✳   home corner activities (A8, A9, B1, D8, F6, F7,
          F9, F10, G10, H5, H7, H9)
✳   'Who am I?' games (B10, F7, H4)
✳   feely bags (A5, F6)
✳   memory games (A10)
✳   what's in the parcel? (F2)
✳   senses games (A5, A7, A9, F6)
✳   guessing games (C10, F2)
✳
✳
✳

Planned activities

This section is subdivided into the following 12 areas of learning, each identified by a letter:

A All about people
B Animals
C Plants, leaves and flowers
D Out of doors
E Exploring materials
F Joining materials
G Changing materials (food)
H Variety of materials
I Light and colours
J Sound
K Movement and forces
L Electricity

Each area is matched to the appropriate early learning goals and the content area in the National Curriculum so as to provide a transition from early learning goals to the next stage of schooling.

For each area of learning there are 10 sets of activities for based on the learning needs of young children. The activities provide children with a wide variety of new experiences while maintaining carefully planned breadth and balance as well as continuity and progression.

The Purpose, Resources, and Safety points are meant for guidance for practitioners working with a group of children.

The Challenge at the bottom of the page can provide a focal point for the activity for the children. The challenges could be written on cards, and the cards used as support material for the adult supervising the activity, as part of a display and/or to enhance early reading skills.

There is an Assessment question on each page to help you to assess what children have learned from the activities.

The last activity in each area can be used as an assessment activity. The questions are matched to the yellow (Y), blue (B), green (G) and grey (ELG) bands in the *Curriculum Guidance for the Foundation Stage*. Children who are able to respond to the requirements of the last question are meeting the early learning goals and are ready to move forward to the next stage in their learning.

Tommy Thumb, Tommy Thumb, where are you?

Purpose
* To be familiar with the joints and actions of fingers and thumb

Resources
* Finger puppets
* Tiny hats

Activities
* Sing 'Tommy Thumb, where are you?' Make Tommy dance. Take him for a walk along the table, carpet, through the grass, to meet model farm animals, vehicles, etc.

* What can you pick up with one hand?

Assessment
* Can he/she use fingers and thumbs accurately?

Challenge
Can you take Tommy Thumb for a walk?

Make paper people

Purpose
* To observe and discuss parts of the body
* To compare length of limbs, counting pairs and adding vocabulary

Resources
* Lengths of wallpaper
* Felt-tip pens

Activities
* Ask a boy and a girl to lie down on lengths of wallpaper. Draw around them and cut out the shapes. Use as a display.

* Discuss parts of the body, compare sizes of parts of the body, eg shoulder and waist, length of an arm and a leg, size of the head compared to the body.

* Make labels to pin on to the display.

Assessment
* Can he/she name simple body parts?

Challenge
Which parts of your body can you name?

Do you have a happy face?

Purpose
✳ To observe closely the features on a face and their positions

Resources
✳ Plastic mirrors
✳ Paper plates
✳ Plastic bottles
✳ Balloons
✳ Decorative materials (eg scraps of fabric, pipe cleaners, card, paper, glue, etc)

Activities
✳ Look in a mirror to observe features. Match hair colour to strands of wool or other materials.

✳ Provide a wide range of materials for children to use to add the features, eg pipe cleaners for eyebrows and round balloons for noses. (Push the neck of the balloon through the centre of the plate and fasten to an empty plastic bottle, press the bottle and the balloon will slightly inflate, making the nose grow!)

✳ Try positioning different cut-out mouths on the face to make it appear to cry, frown, be angry, smile, etc.

Safety
✳ Care! Don't allow children to put balloons in their mouths for fear of inhalation.

Assessment
✳ Is he/she able to match facial expressions to feelings?

 Challenge
Can you pull a funny face?

Can we hear you?

Purpose
* To appreciate that we can make a range of sounds with various parts of the body

Resources
* Tape-recorder
* Blindfold

Activities
* Challenge the children to make three different sounds with their hands, feet, legs, voices, etc. Record these and ask other children how they think they were made.

* Blindfold children in turn and ask them to guess how a friend has made a sound.

Safety
* Care! Some children do not like wearing a blindfold.

Assessment
* Is he/she able to make different sounds?

Challenge
What can you hear?

Are you Mr Tickle?

Purpose
* To develop the observation skill of touch

Resources
* Feathers
* Blindfold
* Feely bag with small items in it

Activities
* Ask children wearing a blindfold if they can feel where and when a feather is touching them. Are some parts of their body more sensitive than others? Are they ticklish everywhere?

* Use feely bags for children to guess what is in the bag.

Safety
* Care! Some children do not like wearing a blindfold.

Assessment
* Can they name unseen objects through touch?

Challenge
Are you Mr Tickle?

Different ways to move over things

Purpose
* To explore ways of moving across and over apparatus

Resources
* PE apparatus

Activities
* Challenge the children to move along the floor, across the grass or up and down a climbing frame using different parts of their bodies.

* What can they do as a pair – joined by holding hands, a ribbon, a hoop or a quoit?

Assessment
* Can he/she move confidently across PE apparatus?

Challenge
How many ways can you move over things?

Developing a sense of smell

Purpose
✳ To develop the sense of smell and to appreciate cleanliness

Resources
✳ Pots with tight-fitting lids
✳ A range of common bathroom materials, eg toothpaste, soap, perfume, talc, handcream

Activities
✳ Make up a set of pots with samples of smelly materials in them. Put lids on the pots and number them. Ask the children to match the pots to the selection of materials provided. Liquid smells can be kept on cotton-wool balls or pieces of paper towel.

Extension/variation
✳ Use books impregnated with smells.

Safety
✳ Care! This activity provides an opportunity to talk about the danger of smelling some substances.

Assessment
✳ Is he/she able to discuss the products identified through smell and their uses?

Challenge
What's that smell?

Growing up

Purpose
* To appreciate long-term change
* To realize that as they grow they alter and are able to do different things
* To develop an awareness of time

Resources
* Photographs of themselves from the time they were born
* Baby books
* Baby clothes
* Baby brought to school
* Photograph albums
* Factual books
* Dolls, prams, scales, nappies, etc for 'baby clinic' in role-play area

Activities
* Put photographs in order. Look at reference books to help with the sequencing.

* Peg clothes along a clothes line from birth to present day. Talk about what they can do now, that a baby cannot do.

* Try role-play, starting as a baby and changing slowly, walking, talking, etc.

* Sit in a small group with a mother and her baby and talk about what the baby can do compared to other babies that the group know. Can they watch it being fed, bathed, etc? Look at the special toys and clothes and talk about them.

Extension/variation
* Provide a baby clinic in the role-play area.

Assessment
* Can he/she tell the story of his/her life so far with the aid of a baby book or photo album?

Challenge
Are you the same as you were yesterday?

Are you well?

Purpose
✳ To encourage children to wash their hands

Resources
✳ Soap
✳ Warm water
✳ Towels
✳ Bread
✳ White paper
✳ Forehead crystal thermometers
✳ Access to hot and cold water
✳ Equipment to set up 'hospital' in role-play area
✳ Stethoscope

Activities
✳ Ask the school nurse to talk about germs and hygiene. Let the children dirty their hands then press them onto white bread. Observe the dirt that you *can* see and explain about what you cannot see. Let them wash their hands and press them on white paper or the other side of the slice of bread.

✳ Set up a hospital in the role-play area.

✳ How hot are you? Use forehead crystal thermometers. Place hands in cold, warm and hand-hot water to experience the differences. Use a large nursery thermometer with no scale. Use a word scale.

✳ Use a stethoscope and listen to each other's heart beat.

Assessment
✳ Does he/she know when they must wash their hands?
✳ Can he/she find his/her heart beat with a stethoscope?

Challenge
Are your hands dirty?

Memory games

Purpose

✴ To encourage observation skills and memory retention

Resources

✴ A variety of items on a tray
✴ Cloth
✴ Photographs

Activities

✴ Allow the children to look at and handle the items then cover the tray with a cloth. How many things can they remember? Add more items as the children gain confidence.

✴ Discuss their memories and feelings. Ask them to talk about special times in their lives. Ask them to say how they felt at Christmas time, when they first came to school, their birthday or a holiday. Include any multi-cultural traditions that are relevant to the class. What can they remember about last week, yesterday, and what they have already done today? Develop the idea of memory.

Assessment

Y   Is he/she interested in the items on the tray?
B   Does he/she understand the aims and rules of the game? Does he/she participate?
G   Can he/she talk about what is on the tray?
ELG Can he/she name some of the items afterwards? Can he/she draw some?

Challenge

Have you got a good memory?

Pets

Purpose
* To observe similarities and differences in animals

Resources
* Pet shop
* Pictures/photographs of animals
* Plastic animals
* Soft toys
* Equipment for pet shop: animal food, bedding, cages, etc

Activities
* Visit a pet shop. Look at the different colours of birds, furry animals and fish. Talk about what each animal needs: food, habitat, care, warmth, etc. Look at animal foodstuff and match it to each animal.

* In the classroom make collage pictures and/or look at photographs of the animals.

* Make a pet shop using toy animals, food, bedding, cages, etc.

Safety
* Wash hands before and after handling animals.
* Beware of any problems with asthma and allergies.
* Ensure proper child:adult ratio for the visit.

Assessment
* Can he/she point to a named pet on a picture?

Challenge
What do you know about pets?

Watch the tadpoles

Purpose
* To observe changes in living things
* To learn to use a magnifier

Resources
* Aquarium
* Frog-spawn
* Books

Activities
* Watch the changes from frog-spawn to frogs.

* Use factual books to see the changes in photographs or on drawings.

* Use magnifiers for a close look at the frog-spawn and tadpoles.

* Make a zigzag book of pictures as a record of the changes.

Safety
* Return the frogs to the area from which the frog-spawn was collected.

Assessment
* Can he/she put in order a series of pictures of the changes from frog-spawn to frog?

Challenge
What happens to the tadpoles?

Birds

Purpose
✳ To observe and name the types of birds that are seen in the locality
✳ To learn to use a computer for research

Resources
✳ Charts for identification and discussion of differences in size, shape and markings on the birds
✳ Bird table and nut hangers
✳ Observation station
✳ Computer
✳ CD-Rom identifying birds
✳ Bird cake ingredients: bread, biscuits, nuts and lard; plastic tub, string and large beads
✳ Round inflated balloons
✳ Paper and glue
✳ Tissue paper
✳ Elastic

Activities
✳ Place a bird table and nut containers close to a window. Watch the birds. Create a 'hide' to watch in comfort. Cut out peep lines in a large sheet of dark paper and stick over low windows.

✳ Use a CD-Rom to identify birds.

Extensions/variations
✳ Make bird 'cake'. Melt the lard, then let the children stir in the dry ingredients. Help the children to fasten a large bead securely onto the end of a piece of string. Place in the bottom of a plastic tub, with the string as a wick. Fill the container with the mixture, making sure that the string is central. When cold, remove the tub and hang outside.

✳ Make bird models by covering balloons with papier-mâché. Add wings and a tail with tissue paper. Hang from elastic to make them bob about.

Assessment
✳ Can he/she name two different birds?

Challenge
What do birds eat?

Snails

Purpose
* To observe snails and learn about their normal habitat

Resources
* Empty aquarium or plastic sweet jars
* Snails
* Soil, fresh damp leaves, apple
* Black paper
* Chalk or white crayon
* String
* Clear plastic board
* Plastic interlocking bricks
* Plasticine

Activities
* Go on a snail hunt.

* Back in the classroom, recreate the snails' habitat in an aquarium or plastic sweet jar. Make sure it does not dry out.

* Use black paper for the snails to move across. If the snails are uncooperative, a gentle dip in shallow warm water will lubricate them and encourage movement. Mark the trail with chalk or a white crayon. Measure the trail with a piece of string.

* Place a snail on a clear plastic board. Watch it from underneath. Look at how it moves.

* Have a snail race using plastic interlocking bricks as track walls.

Extension/variation
* Show the children how to put balls of Plasticine on each index finger and pretend they are snail eyes. Move them around. Talk about what the snail can see.

Safety
* Return the snails to where you found them when you have finished with them.

Assessment
* Does he/she know where to find a snail?

Challenge
Does a big snail move faster than a little snail?

Woodlice

Purpose
* To extend the children's knowledge of living things

Resources
* Woodlice
* Plastic sweet jar
* Tray
* Sand
* Soil
* Paper
* Water
* Food for woodlice: twigs, bark, dried leaves
* Adventure park materials: sawdust, sand, sticks, stones, etc

Activities
* Collect woodlice. Keep them in a plastic sweet jar on its side, with food and shelter.

* Observe what happens when one meets another. Will the woodlice travel over soil, paper, water, etc?

* Can they hear if you clap?

* What do they eat?

Extension/variation
* Make a woodlice adventure park in the sand tray with paths and different places to explore.

Safety
* Return the woodlice to where you found them when you have finished with them.

Assessment
* Can he/she talk about woodlice?

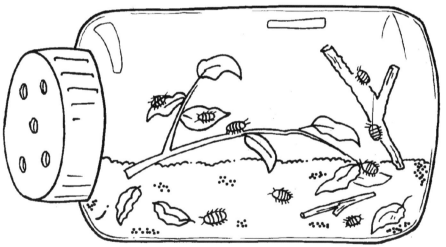

Challenge
What happens when one woodlouse meets another?

What's in the pond?

Purpose
* To appreciate the variety of living things in pond water

Resources
* Bucket
* Plastic aquarium
* Hand lenses
* White plastic tubs
* Identification charts/books, CD-Roms

Activities
* These activities can take place either on site or in the classroom. (Use a bucket to collect pond water and fill a plastic aquarium.)

* Use a hand lens to observe the variety of living things in fresh water. Notice how they move about.

* White containers or lids are useful as small creatures are easily seen against white.

* Use pictures, books, a CD-Rom or charts to identify the creatures.

Safety
* Take care if children are pond-dipping. There must be adequate adult supervision. Children must sit or kneel down when close to the edge and not lean over. Warn of the dangers of drowning.

Assessment
* Can he/she observe and discuss the variety of creatures they see?

 Challenge
What's in the water?

Incy Wincy spider

Purpose
* To appreciate the variety of living things

Resources
* Pictures, video or CD-Rom of spiders to talk about
* Captive spiders
* To make home for spider: plastic sweet jar, twig, Plasticine, cotton wool
* Plasticine and eight plastic straws, or wool pom-poms and eight pipe cleaners
* Elastic
* Large cardboard tube
* String
* Weight
* Table tennis ball
* Water tray

Activities
* Watch spiders to see how they move on the video.

* Go outside and look for spider webs. Watch a spider make a web. Make a home for the spider (see diagram).

* Say the rhyme 'Incy Wincy spider'.

* Make spider models using a ball of Plasticine with eight plastic straw legs, or wool pom-poms with pipe cleaner legs. Fasten to a length of elastic to bob up and down.

* Use a large cardboard tube as a pipe and ask the children if they could help Incy Wincy climb out. Use a model attached to a piece of string with a weight on the end. As the weight is dropped outside the tube the spider will shoot up inside.

Extension/variation
* Make a model spider with a table tennis ball. Use the water tray to explore how the spider will float and rise up when the tube is filled with water.

Safety
* Put the spiders outside when you have finished with them.

Assessment
* Can he/she recognize and name a spider?

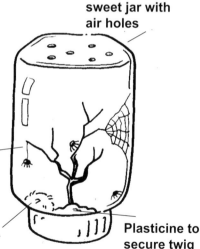

upturned plastic sweet jar with air holes

twig

ball of damp cotton wool for moisture

Plasticine to secure twig

Challenge
Can you help Incy Wincy spider?

Milk products

Purpose
✳ To raise awareness of the variety of farm animals that produce milk, and the range of milk products available

Resources
✳ Toy farm buildings
✳ Toy farm animals
✳ Food products derived from milk: yoghurt, cream, etc
✳ Milk: whole, semi-skimmed, skimmed, long-life
✳ Milkshake ingredients (see below)
✳ Container with a tight-fitting lid
✳ Pinch of salt
✳ Biscuits (for spreading butter on)
✳ Sheep and/or goat's milk (optional)
✳ Books and CD-Roms

Activities
✳ Build a model farm with the children. Talk about the animals.

✳ Make a display of food products derived from milk. Taste the difference between whole milk, semi-skimmed, skimmed and long-life milk. Try milk from sheep and goats if available.

✳ Have milkshakes. Either use commercially packaged milkshakes, or make your own. Let the children choose from a variety of safe food colourings and crushed fruit, eg banana, strawberry, raspberry, apple.

✳ Make butter by putting half a pint of full-fat milk or single cream into a container with a tight-fitting lid. Let the children shake until the whey and curds separate. Remove the curds, add a pinch of salt and spread on biscuits to eat.

Extensions/variations
✳ Ask a local milkman to come to school and talk about how the milk is packaged and delivered.

✳ Research milk in books and on CD-Roms, from the cow to the breakfast table (milk and butter).

Assessment
✳ Can he/she use toy farm animals and vehicles to demonstrate how milk reaches the breakfast table?

Challenge
Where does milk come from?

How many wings does a butterfly have?

Purpose
✳ To observe and record findings by making models

Resources
✳ *The Very Hungry Caterpillar* by Eric Carle (Puffin Books)
✳ Pictures/photographs of butterflies, CD-Rom or video
✳ Tights
✳ Newspaper
✳ Tissue paper or net
✳ Pipe cleaners
✳ Black paint

Activities
✳ Introduce the topic by reading *The Very Hungry Caterpillar*. Spend time discussing the last page with the class.

✳ Observe butterflies flying. Look at pictures, video or CD-Rom. Discuss the number of antennae, legs and wings.

✳ Stuff the leg of an old pair of tights with newspaper. Paint black. Drop paint spots onto tissue paper or net to make the four wings. Add six legs and two antennae using large pipe cleaners.

Assessment
✳ Can he/she make an accurate representation of a butterfly?

Challenge
Can you make a butterfly?

Noah's ark and pairs of animals

Purpose
∗ To raise awareness of the variety of animals
∗ To develop sorting and grouping skills (counting in twos)

Resources
∗ Model ark and toy animals
∗ Bible story book
∗ Modelling materials
∗ PE hoops
∗ Reference books/CD-Roms

Activities
∗ Sing the song 'Who built the ark?'

∗ Act out the story with the children standing on a carpet to represent the ark, moving in pairs, miming the different animals.

∗ Play games, sorting and making sets of animals using modelling materials.

∗ Divide animals into sets using different attributes, eg colour, size, number of legs. Use PE hoops to sort.

∗ Find pairs of animals, either toy models or pictures.

∗ Guessing game – choose an animal and mime how it moves for the other children to guess.

Assessment
Y   Does he/she show interest and curiosity and want to handle the animals?

B   Can he/she put the animals in pairs and manipulate the models?

G   Can he/she examine the animals and put them in different categories?

ELG Can he/she identify some of the features of the animals and communicate these through mime, drawings, paintings or by matching them to pictures on a CD-Rom?

Challenge
How many pairs of animals can go inside the ark?

Leaves of all shapes and sizes

Purpose
✳ To encourage observation skills, including size, pattern and shape

Resources
✳ Leaves
✳ Clear sticky-back plastic
✳ Paint
✳ Paper

Activities
✳ Go outside and collect sets of leaves.

✳ Cover them with plastic to preserve them and make them easy to handle.

✳ Make sets of leaves. Sort by shape, size, colour, etc.

✳ Put a set in order from longest to shortest. Rearrange the set to indicate the narrowest to the widest.

Extensions/variations
✳ Draw round the leaves and cut out leaf shapes.

✳ Make sets of different shaped leaves.

✳ Make leaf prints using paint.

Safety
✳ Some leaves have a sap that can irritate the skin.

Assessment
✳ Can he/she choose a set of similar leaves?

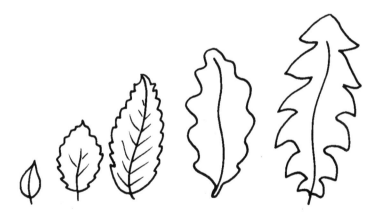

✴ Challenge
Find the longest leaf.

Recording leaf shapes

Purpose
* To observe similarities and differences in leaf shapes, textures and colours
* To match colours
* To identify leaves using books and CD-Roms

Resources
* Fat wax crayons
* Leaves
* Reference books/CD-Roms

Activities
* Choose a leaf to rub. Look at the top and underneath surface of the leaf. Discuss the differences. Introduce new vocabulary – *veins*, *stalk*, *leaf*, *leaflets*. Compare leaf shapes and colours.

* Demonstrate how to make a rubbing of a leaf. Encourage the children to choose colours that are similar to the leaf. Cut out the leaf rubbings and make a display.

* Use CD-Roms and reference books to identify types.

Assessment
* Is he/she able to discuss shapes and compare leaves?

Challenge
Do you know how to make a leaf rubbing?

Growing plants from seeds

Purpose
* To observe growth over time
* To increase mathematical and scientific vocabulary
* To compare and measure
* To learn to use garden tools

Resources
* Plant pots
* Garden tools
* Marigold seeds
* Sunflower seeds
* Nasturtium seeds
* Sweetpea seeds
* String or strips of paper
* Camera and/or drawing/painting materials

Activities
* Plant a variety of seeds in a garden or (labelled) plant pots and watch them grow.

* Keep a chart to show the rate of growth. Measure the plants with string or strips of paper every two days and use them to make a chart.

* Take photographs and ask the children to paint or make drawings of their plants.

* Compare the height of the plant with the children who grew it. Which grows more quickly? Keep a diary of growth.

Assessment
* Can he/she draw themselves and his/her plant, with a clear understanding of size?

 Challenge
Who can grow the tallest plant?

Jack and the beanstalk

Purpose
* To observe the plant life cycle
* To consolidate mathematical understanding of length
* To develop a sense of changes and time

Resources
* Runner bean seeds
* Grow-bags or plant pots
* Garden tools
* Ruler
* Canes or other supports
* Green wool
* Green paper

Activities
* Tell the story of Jack and the beanstalk.

* Plant runner bean seeds and observe them growing. Look for the first leaf, tendril, flower and bean. Measure the beanstalk daily. Examine the tendrils and see how they wind round supports.

* Open a bean and examine the seeds. Discuss the life cycle.

* Make a beanstalk to record what the children see and say. Use green wool as a stalk and cut out green paper leaves. Use the leaves to write new words, eg *stalk*, *leaf*, *flower*, *tendril*, *pod*, *seed*. Arrange the leaves in pairs up the stalk. Ask the children to tell you something they know about plants. Write what they say on a leaf and add their name.

Extensions/variations
* Count in twos along the leaves.

* Cook and eat some beans

Assessment
* Can he/she talk about the different parts of the bean plant?

Challenge
How tall can you make Jack's beanstalk?

Mary, Mary, quite contrary

Purpose
✳ To observe the difference between living and non-living things

Resources
✳ Garden area
✳ Tub or grow-bag
✳ Watering can
✳ Shells (real)
✳ Seeds
✳ Plants
✳ Pasta shells
✳ Paper
✳ Glue

Activities
✳ Begin with the nursery rhyme 'Mary, Mary, quite contrary'.

✳ Make a garden with the children. Sow the seeds. Add shells for decoration. Ask the children what they think will happen. Talk about the differences in plants, seeds and shells. Which do they think are alive? After a week, look again to see any changes.

Extension/variation
✳ Make a collage picture using real and pasta shells.

Assessment
✳ Can he/she make sets of living, once-lived and never-been-alive objects?

Challenge
Can you make a garden grow, like Mary?

Growing bulbs

Purpose
* To observe changes from a bulb to a plant
* To develop a sense of time passing

Resources
* Amaryllis lily bulb and pot
* Sticks and coloured paper
* Onions
* Hyacinth bulbs or other spring bulbs
* Compost and pots
* Clear container in which to grow bulb
* Camera

Activities
* Let the children handle the amaryllis lily bulb and discuss what they think it is. Plant the bulb and observe the changes over time. Let the children make models using sticks and coloured paper.

* Cut an onion in half so that they can see the inside and peel the layers away.

* Plant spring bulbs in damp compost in pots. Store in the dark until the leaves are through and the top of the flower bud is showing.

* Grow a hyacinth in water to show them the root system developing. Keep a diary or photographs to record the growth.

Safety
* It is preferable to use a plastic container rather than glass to grow the hyacinth, for safety reasons.

Assessment
* Can he/she make a model plant, with leaves, stem, flowers, bulb and root?

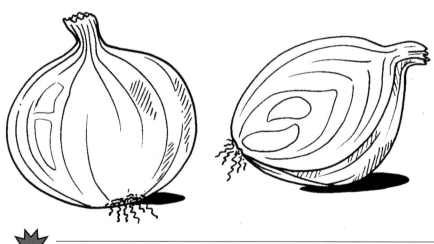

Challenge
What is inside a bulb?

Plastic bottle greenhouses

Purpose
* To understand the conditions needed for growth

Resources
* 2 litre clear plastic bottles
* Scissors to cut plastic
* Masking tape
* Compost
* Small plants, eg Busy Lizzie or ivy

Activities
* Use two similar bottles for each 'greenhouse'. Cut them in half and discard the top halves. (Stick masking tape round the bottle where you wish to cut it; this makes the cutting safer and more accurate.)

* Let the children put compost in the bottom of one and plant a small plant. Add enough water to make it damp. Place the second half over the top. It should be a tight fit.

* The enclosed plant should grow for a long time without being opened or watered.

Assessment
* Can he/she make a complete greenhouse?

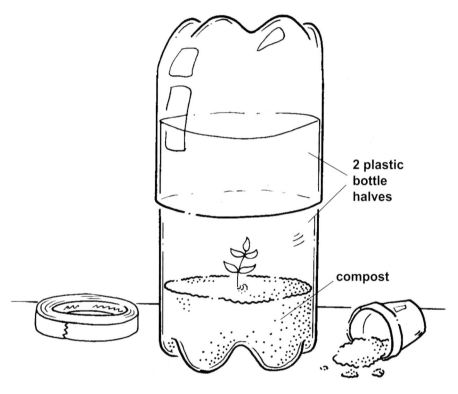

2 plastic bottle halves

compost

Challenge
Can you make a garden in a bottle?

Make a seed mosaic

Purpose
* To observe the variety of seeds
* To develop designing skills

Resources
* Have a collection of untreated seeds, eg beans, peas, nasturtiums, rice, marigold, grass, carrot, mustard and cress
* Hand lenses
* Playdough or Plasticine
* Coffee jar lid

Activities
* Use hand lenses to observe the different textures, sizes, colours, shapes of seeds. Discuss what they would grow into, and that some of them are food.

* Create a pattern with the seeds. Use a bed of playdough or Plasticine pressed into a coffee jar lid.

Safety
* Seeds are frequently treated with poisonous substances.

Assessment
* Is he/she able to choose a range of seeds to create a pattern?

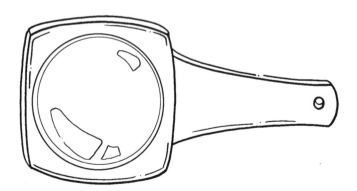

✴ Challenge
Can you make a seed pattern?

Our food

Purpose
* To understand the origins of some food
* To find out about food

Resources
* Plate of dinner, or a sandwich and a drink
* Potatoes, crisps, coffee beans and coffee, pea pods, mange-touts, tinned peas, frozen peas, mushy peas, dried peas, tea leaves, etc
* Bag
* Saucepan, water and stove top
* Hot oil (adult only!)
* Potato peeler (for adult), saucepan, masher
* Books on food farming and food manufacturing

Activities
* Start with a plate of dinner, or a sandwich and a drink. Provide the range of foods and ask the children to put them in sets.

* Give each child a potato to look at carefully. Introduce the correct vocabulary – *skin*, *eyes*, *root*. Put all of the potatoes back in a bag and challenge the children to pick out the one that they looked at.

* Make crisps for the children and mashed potatoes with the children. Let them mash the potatoes after watching an adult peel and cook them.

* Let the children handle frozen peas and dried peas, then cook and eat some. Do they taste the same?

Assessment
* Does he/she understand that a potato is grown in the ground and is made into many forms to be eaten?

Challenge
What is a crisp made from?

Harvest festival

Purpose
✳ To reinforce knowledge of plants, their uses and life cycle

Resources
✳ Harvest festival produce: fruits, vegetables, seeds
✳ Paint, paper, crayons and other art materials

Activities
✳ Make a display of fruits and seeds.

✳ Sort fruit and vegetables by colour, size or texture. Discuss the feel, smell, appearance, etc.

✳ Sort the fruit and vegetables by what was grown on trees and bushes, on plants or under the ground. Add labels.

✳ Make prints with paint, draw unusual fruits, and taste some, raw and cooked (if appropriate).

✳ Make a harvest festival display. Ask the children to place a note on each fruit or vegetable giving its name, origin and use.

✳ Choose two fruit or vegetables and ask the group to say what is different about them, and what is the same.

✳ Have a guessing game: 'I am thinking of …' with attributes of a specific fruit, etc. Children have to choose what they think you are describing.

Assessment
Y   Does he/she show an interest and handle a range of harvest produce?
B   Can he/she sort by colour, size or texture?
G   Does he/she comment on the feel, smell, taste, appearance of fruits?
ELG Can he/she find similarities and differences, find patterns and compare shape and size? Can he/she record his/her findings?

 Challenge
How many different fruits and vegetables can you find?

Look down

Purpose
✳ To explore the plants, animals and materials that are on the ground

Resources
✳ Collecting trays
✳ Hand lenses
✳ Waterproof sheet
✳ Stones, soil, flowers, leaves, etc

Activities
✳ Ask the children to sit or lie on the ground on a dry day and to put their heads close to the ground. What does the world look like from that angle? Can they describe the view from there, the things that look big, and the colours that they can see?

✳ Recreate a small scene using a tray and stones, soil, flowers and leaves.

Assessment
✳ Can he/she create a miniature world?

Challenge
Can you make a tiny garden?

Ladybird, ladybird, fly away home

Purpose
✳ To appreciate the sounds, sights and smells from a small perspective

Resources
✳ Model ladybirds made by the children
✳ Rhyme: Ladybird, ladybird, fly away home
✳ *The Bad-tempered Ladybird* by Eric Carle (Puffin Books) as an alternative starting point

Activities
✳ Begin with the rhyme. Ask children to pretend that their hand is a ladybird. Take it on a journey, across the playground, through the grass, in the flowers and bushes, looking for a home.

✳ Create a wall display with moveable leaves. Ask the children to draw and cut out pictures of ladybirds to stick somewhere on the display.

Assessment
✳ Is he/she able to concentrate and respond to a different perspective?

Challenge
Can you find a ladybird?

Look up

Purpose
✳ To raise awareness of the changing sky

Resources
✳ Large plastic mirrors
✳ Paints and/or drawing materials
✳ Black and white photographs of daytime and night-time scenes

Activities
✳ On a bright, windy day look at the clouds. Talk about the colour, shape and speed at which they are travelling. What else can be seen? Look for birds, aeroplanes, trees waving, smoke, flags, etc.

✳ Compare the day sky and the night. Make two contrasting pictures. Use a black and white photograph of a daytime scene.

✳ Watch the movement of the birds. Mime the different flight patterns.

✳ Make mobiles of things that move in the sky.

✳ Use the mirrors to look at the sky. Place a large mirror on the ground. Sit a group of children round the mirror and talk about what they can see.

Safety
✳ Warn children never to look directly at the sun. It is safer to place a large mirror on the ground so that the children are looking down. Be careful of bright reflections.

Assessment
✳ Is he/she able to create a mobile or draw/paint a picture of the sky?

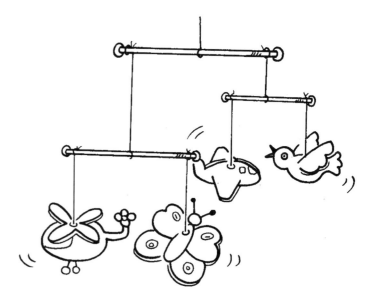

Challenge
What is over your head?

Can you see the wind?

Purpose
∗ To encourage the children to think about an invisible force, and its effects

Resources
∗ Windmills
∗ Streamers
∗ Flags
∗ Paper leaves
∗ Plastic carrier bags

Activities
∗ On a windy day go outside and watch streamers blowing. Feel the effect of the wind on their faces and clothes. Watch the trees and plants move in the wind.

∗ Can the children be the wind, and make a paper leaf move by blowing? Can they catch air in a plastic carrier bag?

Assessment
∗ Give out windmills, flags and streamers. Can he/she explain what makes them move?

Challenge
Can you catch the wind?

Who lives at the zoo?

Purpose
* To extend knowledge of living things in the wider world
* To develop designing and making skills

Resources
* Books, models, videos, pictures for reference
* *The Enormous Crocodile* by Roald Dahl (Puffin Books)
* Toy zoo animals
* Plasticine and/or playdough
* Card, paints, etc to make masks
* Face paints
* Fabrics with fur, spots, stripes, etc

Activities
* Read *The Enormous Crocodile*.

* Sing 'We're all going to the zoo tomorrow'.

* Make a model of a zoo using plastic animals. Make animals with Plasticine and playdough. Discuss the relative sizes of animals.

* Look in books to find pictures of zoo animals.

Extensions/variations
* Ask the children to imitate the animals.

* Create masks or use face paints. Add tails and fabrics with fur, spots, stripes, etc.

Assessment
* Is he/she able to name a number of zoo animals?
* Can he/she make a simple 'home' for an animal?

Challenge
How many pictures of zoo animals can you find?

What is it?

Purpose
* To develop observation and descriptive skills
* To identify features

Resources
* Set of animal or plant picture cards or models and a set of matching cards with a description on each one, eg otter: *it is covered in fur, eats fish and lives in a river*

Activity
* Spread out the cards or models and talk about each one. Ask the children to choose one and to tell you what they know about it. Use the cards as a matching or guessing game.

Assessment
* Is he/she able to identify features of animals or plants?

Challenge
Can you play the animal game?

Where does it live?

Purpose
* To develop the idea that plants are grown in different places

Resources
* Pictures and plants, eg carrot, banana, seaweed, apple

Activity
* Have a set of pictures of different habitats, eg orchard, desert, lake, sea, vegetable garden, field, wood. Ask the children to match an apple, box of dates, bull-rush, seaweed, cabbage, carrot, rose, pine cone, etc to the appropriate picture.

Assessment
* Is he/she able to distinguish between different types of places where plants are found (eg desert, by the sea, woodland, etc)?

Challenge
Where do plants live?

Where do you go for a holiday?

Purpose
✳ To think about the wider world
✳ To learn to use maps

Resources
✳ *Topsy and Tim Go on Holiday* by Jean Adamson (Ladybird Books)
✳ Holiday brochures, postcards, photographs, etc for travel agent's in role-play area
✳ Plain card
✳ Range of pencils, sharpeners and erasers
✳ Suitcases
✳ Clothes for different types of holiday
✳ Catalogues with pictures of clothes
✳ ICT program: *Dressing Teddy* (My World)
✳ Postcards from a wide variety of places
✳ Maps and atlases

Activities
✳ Read *Topsy and Tim Go on Holiday*. Talk about different places to visit.

✳ Make a travel agent's in the role-play area.

✳ Use plain card for the children to make their own postcards. Provide a range of pencils, sharpeners and erasers for children to select and use when writing postcards.

✳ Pack suitcases for different types of holiday. Alternatively, give the children large pictures of suitcases. They could then cut out pictures from catalogues and stick them on the appropriate case.

✳ Use the ICT program *Dressing Teddy*.

✳ Display postcards from a variety of places and relate these to places on a map and/or atlas.

Assessment
✳ Is he/she able to talk about and compare holidays in different parts of the world?

Challenge
Where would you like to take Teddy on holiday?

Make an underwater world

Purpose
✴ To develop creative skills, designing and making skills, expressing and communicating ideas
✴ To find out about and identify underwater creatures

Resources
✴ *The Rainbow Fish* by Marcus Pfister (North-South Books)
✴ Range of decorative materials, including sequins
✴ Reference books

Activities
✴ You could read *The Rainbow Fish* as a stimulus for the activities.

✴ Make a part of the room into an underwater world. With the children, decide on how to create seaweed. Ask the children to draw and decorate fish shapes using sequins. Hang them on thread to make mobiles.

✴ Ask the children to look in books to see the shapes and colours to use. Include shells, an octopus, crabs, etc.

Assessment
✴ Is he/she able to create a representation of a fish?

Challenge
What is it like under the sea?

We're going on a dinosaur hunt

Purpose
* To extend imagination
* To discuss what is real, what happened in the past

Resources
* Story: *We're Going on a Bear Hunt* by Michael Rosen (Walker Books)
* Plastic model dinosaurs (ask children to bring from home)
* Compost, gravel, clay, or wet and dry sand
* Lego or other interlocking plastic bricks
* Plasticine, playdough and other materials to make model dinosaurs
* Tools for making dinosaurs and dinosaur landscape, eg trowels, plastic cutlery, scissors, glue and glue sticks, etc

Activities
* Read *We're Going on a Bear Hunt* then go outside and act it out as a class.

* Change this to 'We're going on a dinosaur hunt'. Ask the children to bring models to school. Create a dinosaur landscape in the sand tray, using compost, gravel, clay, or wet and dry sand.

* Make model dinosaurs using interlocking plastic bricks, Plasticine or playdough.

Assessment
Y   Does he/she realize that the sand can be used as a landscape?

B   Can he/she join pieces of interlocking plastic bricks together to make model dinosaurs? Does he/she use tools correctly to make the landscape?

G   Is he/she able to use tools, equipment and materials competently and with a purpose in mind?

ELG   Is he/she able to build a model dinosaur and construct a landscape by selecting appropriate resources? Can he/she use tools and techniques to shape, assemble and join materials? Is he/she able to adapt his/her work where necessary?

Challenge
Can you make a model dinosaur?

Water play

Purpose
* To use all the senses to find out about water

Resources
* Water tray
* Aprons
* Variety of utensils and containers (see Water play, page 10)
* *The Cow Who Fell in the Canal* by Phyllis Krasilovsky (Picture Puffin)
* Polystyrene trays
* Model cow or interlocking plastic bricks
* Absorbent and waterproof materials
* Ice cubes and/or ice balloons (fill balloons with cold water from the tap, freeze for 48 hours)

Activities
* Introduce water play by discussing the 'dos and don'ts', ie the class rules on expected behaviour and safe use when at the water tray.

* Allow a group to explore 'What happens when …', 'What happens if …', giving them time to experience the range of ideas listed on page 10. For example, can they find things that sink, things that float on the surface, things that float under the surface, things that float then sink, etc?

* Read the story of the Dutch cow who floated down the canal. Challenge the children to make a raft (polystyrene tray) sink, using a model cow or interlocking plastic bricks.

* Compare materials that absorb water, eg bibs, towels and sponges, and those that are waterproof.

* Fill containers of different sizes and shape. Add jugs, syringes, pipes, etc.

* Use ice balloons, ice cubes and ice lollies; observe how they melt.

Safety
* Be careful of wet, slippery surfaces and solutions in eyes.

Assessment
* Is he/she able to make connections between ice and water?

Challenge
Find five things that will float.

Bubbles

Purpose
✳ To look at similarities and differences in materials
✳ To raise questions

Resources
✳ Water tray
✳ Whisks, slotted spoons, jugs, empty washing-up liquid bottles, etc
✳ Soapflakes
✳ Dark sugar paper

Activities
✳ Part fill the water tray and provide whisks, slotted spoons, jugs and empty washing-up liquid bottles. Allow time for the children to explore the force of the water and the feel of the apparatus in it.

✳ Sprinkle some soapflakes on the water and let the children find out what happens as they dissolve and change in texture. Talk about what has happened. Let them discover that bubbles can be made and enjoy playing with them.

✳ Talk about the washing machine at home and how it works.

✳ Place some bubbles on dark sugar paper and watch them change in shape and size, and pop.

Safety
Be careful of soap in eyes and a slippery floor.

Assessment
✳ Can he/she create bubbles?

Challenge
How can we make bubbles?

Can we mend the bucket?

Purpose
* To learn to use tools and materials correctly

Resources
* Four small plastic buckets: one with a hole in the base, one with a hole in the side near the base, one with a hole in the side near the rim, and one with no holes
* Variety of materials for mending the buckets
* Large plastic bottle
* Knife or other implement (for practioner) to make holes
* Water tray
* Collection of items with holes in them

Activities
* Sing 'There's a hole in my bucket'. Show the children the bucket with the hole in the base. Ask the children for suggestions for how to mend the hole. Allow the children to try out their ideas. Go outside, or work over the water tray.

* Try filling all the buckets, lift them up high and ask the children to observe the spray of water from each. Which bucket will still hold most of the water, which will hold none?

* Make a set of holes down the length of a large clear plastic bottle. Let the children fill it and watch how the jet of water comes out at a different angle from each hole.

Extensions/variations
* Say 'Jack and Jill'.

* Put a collection of things with holes in them to be used with the water.

Assessment
* Is he/she able to offer suitable materials to mend the hole?

 Challenge
How can we mend Jill's bucket?

Soaking up water

Purpose
* To stimulate curiosity and raise questions

Resources
* Water tray
* Small stone
* Dishes
* Sieves
* Sand
* Soil
* Compost

Activities
* Encourage the children to look at themselves in a bowl of water or the water tray. Drop a small stone into the water. What happens to the reflection?

* Go outside after it has been raining. Notice the spots of rain on the plants and the puddles on the ground. Go out again later and see if the water is still there. Where has the puddle gone?

* Let the children make little puddles outside or inside using dishes, sieves, sand, soil, compost. Extend the vocabulary – *dry, damp, moist, wet*.

Assessment
* Is he/she able to comment on the changes in the water?

Challenge
Where has the water gone?

Natural materials

Purpose
* To explore a range of natural materials

Resources
* Sand tray or sand pit
* Resources and equipment (see Sand tray, page 9)

Activities
* Establish the rules for systematic use of this play area.

* Have a theme, eg seaside with dry or damp sand, shells, flags, buckets and spades, or compost, flowerpots, trowels and garden forks.

* Use the range of resources and ideas listed on page 9, developing a new idea, learning and practising new skills each week.

Assessment
* Is he/she able to select and use a number of tools?

Challenge
What can you make today?

Make a touchy tortoise

Purpose
* To explore a range of textures and to describe them

Resources
* Large-scale picture of a tortoise with clearly defined sections on the shell
* A wide range of materials
* Glue
* Scissors
* Blindfold

Activities
* Ask the children to help you make a picture of Tom Tortoise with a touchy shell. Each person must choose a texture that they like and is different to everyone else's. These can be stuck onto the shell sections.

* Let the children feel the different textures. Can they touch a section when blindfolded and then find it when they can see? They can check the guess by touching the sections.

* Talk about the appearance and texture of each section and increase vocabulary.

* Play a 'find me' game. Describe a section and see if the children can find the correct section.

* Let them describe sections for their friends.

Assessment
* Can he/she match pairs of fabric pieces?

Challenge
Can you make a touchy tortoise?

Soft and hard

Purpose
* To encourage children to play with and talk about materials
* To select materials based on a single criterion

Resources
* Soft things: feathers, feather duster or boa, sponges, fabrics, soft toys, cushions and paper tissues
* Hard things: pieces of wood, stone, metal objects and wooden toys
* Books and CD-Rom

Activities
* Allow time for the children to handle all the items. Ask them to put them into hard and soft sets.

* Ask which would be the nicest to lie on, or to cuddle. Are soft things fragile? Can any of the items be squashed? Do they go back into shape? Will they tear easily?

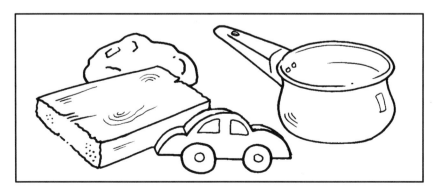

Extension/variation
* Look in books or on a CD-Rom to find pictures of hard and soft things.

Assessment
* Is he/she able to differentiate between hard/soft and strong/weak?

Challenge
Find five soft things and five squashy things.

Smooth and rough

Purpose
✳ To notice, discuss and record pattern and texture

Resources
✳ Coins
✳ Large wax crayons
✳ Paper
✳ Building materials
✳ CD-Rom for reference

Activities
✳ Show the children how to make a rubbing of a coin. Let them practise the technique.

✳ Take them on a walk and let them collect rubbings of different textures and patterns.

✳ Display a set of rubbings in the classroom and ask children to match the rubbing with the real textures. Can they recreate the patterns?

Extensions/variations
✳ Look for patterns and textures on the building materials used inside and outside the room.

✳ Use the CD-Rom to find out about how buildings are constructed.

✳ Make a class book of textures.

✳ Compare coins from different countries.

Assessment
✳ Is he/she able to make a rubbing?

 Challenge
Can you make a rough and smooth pattern?

Are playdough and Plasticine the same?

Purpose
* To explore the difference in properties of two materials using all their senses as appropriate

Resources
* Plasticine
* Playdough
* Tools: modelling boards, forks, sticks, rolling pins, cutters, etc.
* Clay
* Air-dried clay
* Paint and paint brushes

Activities
* Provide pieces of Plasticine and make playdough with the children. Give out modelling boards, forks, sticks, rolling pins and cutters. Let the children handle the materials. Try flattening it, rolling it and making it into a ball. Can they make a model?

* What happens if the models are left overnight? Can the material be returned to a lump? Can the models be painted? What happens if they are handled for a long time?

* Discuss the differences between Plasticine and playdough. Ask them which they would choose if they wanted to keep their model.

Extensions/variations
* Add clay, air-dried clay or other modelling media to widen their experiences.

* Make pots and containers.

Assessment
* Can he/she talk about the differences?

 ## Challenge
What can you make with Plasticine and playdough?

Tidy up time

Purpose
✳ To create sets using a number of criteria chosen by the children

Resources
✳ Variety of materials and items
✳ Boxes, trays or rings

Activities
✳ Ask the children to sort out the mixture of things into sets to tidy them up. Let them choose how they would like them grouped and name each container.

✳ When they have finished, talk about what they have put in each set and why.

Assessment
Y Is he/she interested in handling the items? Can he/she make the decision where to place them?
B Can he/she talk about what they have done, and why?
G Can he/she divide items into two sets based on his/her own criteria?
ELG Is he/she able to sort a range of objects into different containers confidently and easily?

Challenge
How quickly can you sort a box of beads?

Sticking things together

Purpose
✳ To develop the skills of using glue correctly

Resources
✳ Glue – sticks and liquid, spreaders
✳ Strips of coloured paper
✳ Gold paper
✳ Selection of paper: tissue, cellophane, crepe, etc

Activities
✳ Practise using a spreader or glue brush and the correct amount of glue when joining different coloured strips together to make a paper chain.

✳ Say the rhyme 'The king was in his counting house'. Provide lengths of gold paper for crowns and a selection of papers to use as decoration. Let the children experience the difference when gluing tissue, cellophane, crepe and writing paper shapes onto the crowns.

Assessment
✳ Is he/she able to use glue correctly?

 Challenge
Can you make a crown?

Postman's parcels

Purpose
* To introduce a range of tapes and twines for fastening

Resources
* Masking tape
* Sticky tape
* Double-sided tape
* Coloured tape
* Range of strings and twines
* Stamps and printing set
* Items to wrap as parcels
* Strong sugar paper
* Plastic bags
* Wrapping paper

Activities
* Create a post office corner, with Postman Pat and a lot of different items to wrap as parcels.

* Provide a variety of wrapping materials: strong sugar paper, plastic bags and wrapping paper. Ask the children to wrap the items to give to Postman Pat as parcels.

* Talk about the best tapes to use and how to handle them. Let the children wrap parcels, working in pairs. They could add a label and stamp.

* Have a guessing game: 'What's in the parcel?' Sort different items according to who they might be for, eg teddy for baby, hammer for dad, sponge for a friend, plastic flower for gran, computer disc for mum, etc.

Safety
* Take care with plastic bags.

Assessment
* Can he/she tie a bow and knot?

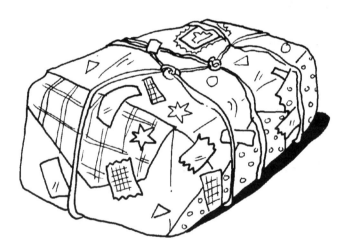

 Challenge
Can you guess what is in the parcels?

Cutting skills

Purpose
* To realize that tools have a specific purpose and to practise using them
* To learn to use scissors carefully and safely

Resources
* Variety of scissors for cutting paper and other materials, left- and right-handed
* Catalogues
* Cotton

Activities
* Draw parallel line pathways on paper. Ask the children to 'drive' along the path with their scissors and cut between the lines.

* Draw shapes with straight, curved and irregular edges. Challenge the children to cut them out along the lines.

* Can they draw and cut out shapes to decorate a clown's outfit?

* Can they choose and cut out an outfit from a catalogue?

* Cut along curled-up snakes using circles of paper, hang them up by threading cotton through the head and watch them turn.

Safety
* Teach how to hold and carry scissors safely. Don't use pointed scissors, but make sure that those available are capable of cutting the materials used.

Assessment
* Is he/she able to use scissors accurately and safely?

Challenge
Can you cut a snake shape?

Working with wood

Purpose
* To give children the experience of working with wood
* To develop the skills to use the tools safely and correctly

Resources
* Bench hooks
* Sawing boards and saws
* Variety of wood, including 8 mm dowel
* Hammer
* Nails
* Screws and screwdrivers

Activities
* Show the children how to hold the tools correctly and how to work safely. Impress on them the need to take care of tools, and to store them correctly.

* Allow them time to try out sawing, holding wood correctly, nailing and joining pieces together.

* Let them design and make something for themselves (watch out for the usual swords and guns!). Model boats and carts work well.

* Teach them the skill of hammering over the leg of the table. This reduces the noise level and is safer.

Safety
* Working with wood does need to be well supervised.

Assessment
* Can he/she cut and use wood safely?

Challenge
What can you make with wood?

Puppet pets

Purpose
* To learn the techniques of making moveable joins

Resources
* String puppet(s)
* Story of Pinocchio or *Bill and Ben* videos
* Paper and card
* Hole punch
* Split pins
* Paper fasteners
* Paper-clips
* Bulldog clips

Activities
* Introduce a string puppet to the children. Talk to the puppet and make it respond through movements. Invite the children to communicate with it. Let them see how the movements are achieved.

* Tell the story of Pinocchio or watch *Bill and Ben* videos. Let them handle and use simple puppets.

* Show the children how to use a hole punch, and let them make snakes with each segment joined to the next by a different fastening.

* Challenge the children to make animals with moving legs. These can be as simple or as complicated as they can manage. Let them design and make an animal of their choice, with as many moving parts as they can.

Extension/variation
* Have a puppet show.

Assessment
* Can he/she make a moveable join?

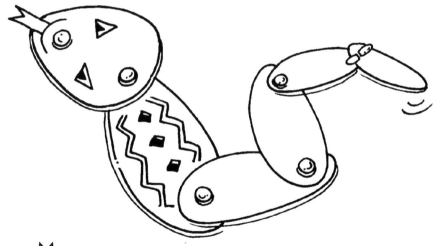

Challenge
Can you make a model animal that can move?

A stitch in time

Purpose
* To develop the skills of stitching, sewing, threading and lacing
* To improve hand–eye coordination and manipulation skills

Resources
* Card
* Laces
* Beads
* Threading needles
* Hole punch
* Felt

Activities
* Use lacing cards with appropriate pictures to thread the laces round. Cut out shoe shapes in thick card, with holes punched, for the children to practise lacing and tying their shoe laces in a bow.

* Use large blunt darning needles and wool for children to sew round letters and numbers.

* Thread beads in patterns of colours, size or shape, or a combination.

* Make beads with playdough or use large manufactured beads and make necklaces, bracelets and other decorations to wear. Have a jeweller's shop.

* Make bags by folding a rectangle of felt in half and stitching up the sides. Add string handles.

* Make a treasure bag by punching holes around the edge of a circle of felt then threading a lace through. Use as a feely bag.

Safety
* Take care with beads, scissors and sharp needles. Teach safe use.

Assessment
* Can he/she stitch correctly?

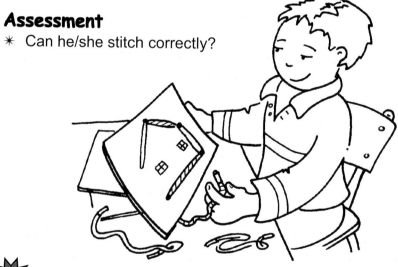

Challenge
What can you thread and lace?

Who am I today?

Purpose
✳ To raise awareness of the fashions and styles of clothes around the world
✳ To practise dressing, manipulating buttons, buckles, press studs, Velcro®, ties, toggles and safety pins

Resources
✳ Clothes from a variety of cultures, with as many different fastenings as possible
✳ Pictures of traditional outfits
✳ Stories from other cultures

Activities
✳ Provide a 'treasure chest' of attractive items of clothing, hats, scarves, bags and jewellery.

✳ Have items of clothing on hangers and have a clothes shop, with a long mirror. Allow time for groups of children to visit the shop and try on the different outfits.

✳ Use different occasions – a wedding, a party, a seaside trip, a world conference, a meeting with the queen, a sports event or a festival. Make sure that there is a strong multi-cultural element. Talk about the different garments and explain when and how they should be worn.

✳ Use henna and face paints. Invite adults in traditional costumes to take part and help with the dressing up. Include pearly kings and traditional Scottish, Irish and English costumes, as well as those from the wider world.

Assessment
✳ Is he/she able to dress without assistance?

 Challenge
Who will you be today?

Construction corner

Purpose
∗ To explore how to construct and disassemble models
∗ To develop spacial awareness and an understanding of how strong connections are made

Resources
∗ Construction kits and bricks
∗ Plastic and paper straws
∗ Pipe cleaners

Activities
∗ Introduce a new construction kit and demonstrate how the pieces join together. Allow time for children to explore for themselves and to make anything they choose.

∗ Add a challenge later, eg make a see-saw, a table and chairs, a train, or pram, etc.

∗ Provide picture instructions and plans for children to follow, to extend their ideas.

∗ Using other materials, can they join them and make models such as a tall tower?

Assessment
∗ Is he/she able to construct a model?

Challenge
What can you build today?

Building site

Purpose
∗ To enable children to handle large pieces of equipment
∗ To extend imaginative play

Resources
∗ Throw-away materials
∗ Large-scale blocks
∗ Bricks
∗ Planks
∗ Poles
∗ Curtains
∗ Large card carpet tubes
∗ Plastic tubs and barrels
∗ Large construction kits
∗ Paint and other decorations

Activities
∗ Ask the children what they would like to make, eg boat or car for them to sit in, a castle or a spaceship, an obstacle course, etc. Work with the children. Plan it with them and ask them to suggest how to make it and what to use.

∗ If fine, work out of doors. Alternatively, use a large space inside.

∗ If using throw-away materials, paint and decorate it, and add flags and other embellishments.

Extension/variation
∗ Give time for the children to role play. When they lose interest, take it to pieces with them and construct something different.

Assessment
∗ Does he/she use imagination well and create own scenario?

 Challenge
Build something large enough to play in.

Workshop corner

Purpose
✳ To practise using their new skills in a different situation

Resources
✳ Throw-away materials
✳ Range of tools and equipment
✳ Construction kit instructions

Activity
✳ Use the role-play area to organize a workshop or factory, and a shop to sell the goods. Ask the children to design and make models and toys that can be 'sold' in the shop. This could be:
- a Father Christmas' workshop near Christmas time
- a garden centre area in the summer, with plants and scarecrows
- a fruit shop with model fruit
- a cake shop with baking ingredients
- a book shop, making books and cards
- a gift shop.

Assessment
Y   Does he/she use tools, eg scissors, correctly?
B   Can he/she cut and join materials and follow instructions to make something?
G   Does he/she plan, select tools and materials to make something? Does he/she use imagination when working with a range of materials? Can he/she use materials and tools appropriately in a new context?
ELG Can he/she build and construct with a wide range of objects, selecting and using materials that are appropriate? Does he/she use tools correctly and safely?

Challenge
Can you make something in the workshop?

Sandwich making

Purpose
* To learn to spread with a knife (not sharp)
* To cut bread
* To learn about hygiene and healthy foods

Resources
* *The Giant Jam Sandwich* by John Vernon Lord (Macmillan Children's Books)
* Sliced bread
* Butter or spread
* Ingredients for sandwiches: jam, meat and fish paste, salad, cheese, egg, honey, etc

Activities
* Read *The Giant Jam Sandwich*. Make real sandwiches and match to the pictures in the book.

* Try taste tests of small pieces of sandwiches. Make a chart of favourite sandwiches.

* Match picture clues of the fillings to jars and pots.

* Have a range of different types of bread for children to talk about, taste and draw.

Extensions/variations
* Investigate what happens when bread is left in a warm place. Why does it go hard?

* Make toast.

* Have a tea party (together with other food items in this section).

Assessment
* Can he/she manipulate a knife safely and correctly?

 Challenge
Who can make the tastiest sandwich?

Baking and making

Purpose
✳ To observe the change from ingredients to a sponge cake
✳ To begin to appreciate irreversible change

Resources
✳ Storybook: *The Tiger Who Came to Tea* by Judith Kerr (Picture Lions)
✳ Microwave oven or oven
✳ Sponge cake ingredients and equipment
✳ Bun cases
✳ Cooking utensils
✳ Icing sugar

Activities
✳ Read *The Tiger Who Came to Tea*.

✳ Make sponge buns with the children, allowing them to measure the ingredients and stir the mixture. Use a microwave if possible so that the children can see the mixture rise.

✳ When the buns are cold, let the children make the icing and spread it on the buns. Discuss the white powder, the clear liquid (water) and the change as it goes solid.

✳ Eat the buns at a tea party (together with other food items in this section).

Safety
✳ Make sure that the utensils are used only for cooking, and that the children wash their hands, wear aprons and do not eat any of the raw mixture.

Assessment
✳ Is he/she able to talk about how a bun is made?

Challenge
Can you make a bun for tea?

Rainbow jelly

Purpose
* To observe the changes from solid cubes, dissolving in the liquid and setting to a solid shape
* To use all the appropriate senses

Resources
* Made-up jelly
* Different coloured jelly mixes
* Small cases
* Basin
* Forks
* Spoons
* Measuring equipment

Activities
* Show the children the made-up jelly. Let them all handle a small piece, to smell it and talk about it. Discard the piece and ask all the children to wash their hands.

* Make jelly with the children. Let the children participate as much as possible, but be careful of hot water.

* Ask them to guess what will happen and how long it will take to set. Do they think different coloured jellies will have a different smell and taste? Each group could make a different flavour.

* Make some small jellies in cases and pour the rest into a large clear bowl. Allow this to set before adding a different colour from the next group.

* Use the small jellies as a taste test.

* Eat the rainbow jelly at a tea party (together with other food items in this section).

Assessment
* Does he/she observe the changes in the jelly?

Challenge
How long does it take to make a jelly?

What do you like for breakfast?

Purpose
✳ To explore the changes in materials – dry to wet

Resources
✳ Porridge oats
✳ 'Instant' hot cereal
✳ Water
✳ Milk
✳ Salt
✳ Sugar
✳ Spoon
✳ Small boxes of cornflakes, muesli, etc
✳ Recipes

Activities
✳ Tell the story of 'The three bears'. Discuss their breakfast and what went wrong.

✳ Make porridge with the children. Let them make 'instant' hot cereal (safer!) using different quantities of milk. Try adding salt or sugar.

✳ Let them observe, feel and taste the differences. What can they tell by feel (stirring with a spoon) and what can they only tell by taste?

✳ Discuss what the children have for breakfast. Which are their favourite cereals? Have small boxes of each. Allow them to feel them and taste them dry, then add water or milk and let them feel the difference in texture. Does the taste change?

Assessment
✳ Is he/she able to distinguish between different tastes?

Challenge
Can you make the three bears some porridge?

Sweet or sour?

Purpose
* To develop the sense and vocabulary of taste
* To observe the change from powder to liquid to solid

Resources
Poem: *Don't Put Mustard in the Custard* by Michael Rosen (Scholastic)
* Custard powder or instant custard
* Sugar
* Milk
* Mustard powder
* Recipes

Activities
* Read *Don't Put Mustard in the Custard*.

* Ask the children to feel custard powder and to describe what it feels like. Add a small amount of water and let them stir it and handle it. Add more water until it will pour.

* Make custard using milk. Let the children measure the ingredients. Take care with boiling the milk. Demonstrate how the custard will run when hot. Let them eat it when it is cold and solid.

* Let them mix mustard powder with water to make mustard. Observe the changes.

Safety
* Demonstrate the making of custard as the milk is boiling. Take care with tasting mustard.

Assessment
* Is he/she able to talk about similarities and differences in texture and taste?

Challenge
Is mustard the same as custard?

What did the three little pigs eat?

Purpose
* To observe changes when cooking

Resources
* Raw vegetables
* Cup-a-soups and other dried packets of vegetable soup
* Tin of vegetable soup
* Can opener
* Heat and saucepan

Activities
* Tell the story of 'The three little pigs'. The pigs put a large pot of soup on the fire to catch the wolf. Talk about the children's favourite soup. Ask what it is made from. Do they think it comes from a packet, a tin or raw ingredients?

* Cook soup using raw vegetables with the children and let them taste it.

* Make vegetable soup from a packet. Observe the ingredients before and after it is made. Can the children guess what the bits are before they are reconstituted?

* Open a tin of vegetable soup, warm and let the children eat it.

Assessment
* Is he/she able to appreciate changes in vegetables from raw, dried, precooked, etc to that tasted in the soup?

Challenge
What does the three little pigs' soup taste like?

Chocolate crispies

Purpose
* To experience the changes in some materials when heated and cooled

Resources
* Chocolate
* Cornflakes
* Butter
* Cheese
* Bread
* Crumbly biscuits
* Chocolate buttons
* Large clear glass bowl
* Saucepan
* Bun cases
* Tin foil case
* Safe heat source, eg hostess tray
* Greaseproof paper
* Spoons

Activities
* Explore what happens to a variety of food when handled. Which stay the same? Which crumble and break, or melt when held in the hand? Sort them into sets.

* Let the children watch while you melt chocolate over a pan of hot water. Take care! Discuss the changes as they happen.

* Let the children stir cornflakes into the melted chocolate and experience the difference in textures. Spoon the mixture into bun cases. Ask the group what they think will happen, and how soon they will be able to eat them.

Extension/variation
* Let the children melt chocolate in a tin foil case on a safe heat source, eg hostess tray. Drop teaspoons of melted chocolate onto a sheet of greaseproof paper and make chocolate drops.

Assessment
* Is he/she able to talk about solid and liquid chocolate?

Challenge
What happens if you warm chocolate?

Fizzy drinks

Purpose
* To begin to understand that there are solids, liquids and gases
* To find out what happens to different solids and liquids when combined

Resources
* Bicarbonate of soda
* Carbonated water
* Lemonade crystals
* Sugar
* 2 litre bottle of lemonade
* Flour (plain and self-raising)
* Water
* Sultanas
* Carbonated drink maker and syrup
* Alka Seltza®
* Tall thin glass
* Natural flavourings

Activities
* Let the children explore what happens when different solids are added to each liquid. Which cause a fizz? Can they hear it? If they put their hand over the container, can they feel it? Talk about what is happening.

* Gently shake a large bottle of lemonade and watch the bubbles rise.

* Use a carbonated drink maker to make carbonated drinks and watch the bubbles. Does the taste change when it has been carbonated? Is there a different sensation in the mouth?

* Drop an Alka Seltza® into a tall thin clear container filled with warm water. Watch the reaction. (Don't let the children drink it.)

* Drop a few sultanas into a 2 litre bottle, filled to the top of the wide part with lemonade. Watch as the sultanas rise when they are covered with bubbles, and fall when the bubbles burst.

* Make fizzy drinks using natural flavourings.

Assessment
* Is he/she able to appreciate that some reactions produce bubbles?

Challenge
Can you make a fizzy drink?

Dissolving – going, going, gone!

Purpose
* To raise awareness that some materials dissolve

Resources
* Stock cubes
* Sugar cubes
* Cubes of potato, bread, cheese, etc
* Saucers, beakers
* Tape-recorder
* Mints
* Juicy fruit sweets

Activities
* Investigate what happens to stock cubes, sugar cubes and other types of cubes if they are:
  * left on saucers
  * left on a damp surface
  * dropped into clear plastic beakers half filled with cold or warm water

* Question the children: What will happen when …? What will happen if …?

* Encourage the children to watch carefully and to comment on the changes as they occur. Tape the comments and play them back afterwards to extend the discussion.

* Give each child a mint and see who can keep it in their mouth for the longest time.

* Give each child a juicy fruit sweet. Does the same happen?

Assessment
* Does he/she make comments and use the term *dissolving* when talking about the mints and juicy fruit sweets?

 Challenge
How long can you keep a mint on your tongue?

Classroom café

Purpose
* To find out more about their own environment
* To develop social skills
* To practise the procedure for laying a table
* To use a computer for word processing

Resources
* Small tables and chairs
* Table cloths
* Plastic knives, forks and spoons
* Plates, dishes, cups, etc
* Salt and pepper pots
* Menus and other café requirements

Activities
* Visit a local café. Talk to the staff about the café. Let each child buy a soft drink there.

* Back at school talk about what they did and saw. Plan to make a café in the classroom, or outside. List all the items needed.

* Give each group a task, eg print patterns on the table cloths, lay the tables, collect flowers for the tables, make the sandwiches, buns or soft drinks, write a menu and price list using the computer, make posters and an open/closed sign.

* Draw up rotas for staff and café-goers. Have a till and money. Invite guests to tea and serve them.

Assessment
* Ensure appropriate child:adult ratio for the visit.

Assessment
Y   Does he/she become involved with the activity and show an interest and curiosity?

B   Does he/she want to be included and participate appropriately?

G   Does he/she talk about the experience, ask questions and make reasoned judgements based on previous experiences?

ELG Can he/she participate at an independent level and make decisions? Is he/she able to discuss the quality of the environment? Have they made it attractive, hygienic and practical? How does it compare to a real café that he/she has visited?

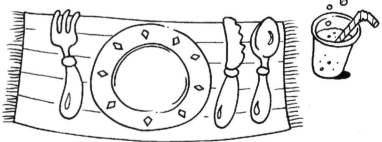

Challenge
What do you need in a café?

Wash day

Purpose
✳ To appreciate that some garments have a specific purpose

Resources
✳ Aprons and overalls, paint shirts, bibs
✳ Cleaning agents
✳ Washing line
✳ Pegs
✳ *Mrs Mopple's Washing Line* by Anita Hewitt (Red Fox)

Activities
✳ After using protective garments for clay or paint work, have a wash day. Ask how we are going to get them clean. Talk about why they need to be clean. Reinforce the system for using aprons etc, making sure that they know the rules.

✳ Let pairs of children try out washing based on their suggestions, eg soap, washing-up liquid, liquid soap, soap powder, different temperatures of water, rubbing, scrubbing or soaking. Allow them to make decisions about how the garments will be dried.

✳ Compare the washed garments. Use a set of bibs each with jam smeared on it, and try different ways of washing. Which is the best?

✳ Read *Mrs Mopple's Washing Line*.

Safety
✳ Take care with hot water, skin irritations and soap in eyes.

Assessment
✳ Is he/she able to wash a bib successfully?

Challenge
Can you wash the clothes clean?

Put your foot in it

Purpose
* To explore the property of stretch
* To talk about foot hygiene
* To practise grouping in pairs

Resources
* Collection of socks and tights of all sizes, colours, types and patterns
* Washing line and pegs
* Large sheets of paper
* Paint or crayons
* Pictures of people who might wear different types of socks

Activities
* Peg one of each pair of socks on a washing line and ask the children to peg the matching sock next to it.

* Peg the smallest tights on a line and ask them to peg up the rest in order of size.

* Investigate which socks and tights will stretch. Let the children draw round a stretched sock and one its normal size. Cut them out and compare sizes.

* Cut out two sock shapes. Ask one child to paint or colour a pattern on one and see if a friend can copy the pattern onto the other.

* Make a collection of different types of socks, eg football, walking, party, bridesmaid, and match them to pictures of people.

* Count in twos.

* Talk about care of feet and toe nails.

Extension/variation
* Near Christmas investigate which sock will hold the most bricks, boxes or presents.

Assessment
* Is he/she able to use the word *stretch* correctly when comparing socks?

Challenge
Which sock stretches the most?

Hands and fingers

Purpose
* To extend counting to fives
* To consolidate work on pairs and symmetry

Resources
* Gloves and mittens of all sizes and for different uses, eg baby, rubber gloves, plastic, motor bike, goal keeper, summer and winter
* Paper
* Paints and crayons
* Textured fabrics and other materials
* Glue

Activities
* Let the children wear one glove/mitten and find the person with the other one. Can they guess what each one is designed for?

* Draw a mitten on one half of a piece of paper and ask the children to paint a pattern on the mitten. Fold the paper to print a symetrical picture. Cut out the pair.

* Cover mitten shapes with textured materials. Ask the children to match pairs of mittens with their eyes closed, by feeling them.

* Give each child a glove with fingers to wear, and hold up when counting as a group in fives.

* Make hand prints with paint and cut out as gloves for a counting display.

Assessment
* Is he/she able to appreciate the amount five?
* Does he/she have a good understanding of two and pairs?

 Challenge
Can you find all the pairs?

Hats on heads

Purpose
* To raise awareness of different materials
* To raise awareness that hats are designed for a specific purpose

Resources
* Hard hats, special hats, baby hats, fez, policeman's helmet, motorbike and bicycle helmets, mitre, hats from all cultures and religions
* Paper
* Equipment and materials to make Easter bonnets/ carnival headgear/shower caps

Activities
* Start with a set of sun hats and caps. Discuss why we need to wear them. Introduce other hats. Ask each person to pick a hat from a hat stand or box, to wear it and say why it is special.

* Have a 'Who am I?' game, using the various hats.

* Encourage the children to think about the purpose and safety aspect of the headgear – bicycle helmet, firefighter's helmet, surgeon's cap, etc.

Extensions/variations
* Ask them to design and make a bicycle helmet or a shower cap for a teddy or doll.

* Make paper Easter bonnets or carnival headgear and display them on blown-up balloons.

Assessment
* Is he/she able to discuss the purpose of a chosen hat?

Challenge
Which is the best hat to wear today?

Shoes and other footwear

Purpose
* To observe size
* To encourage good hygiene and suitable footwear
* To be able to thread laces, tie bows and fasten buckles
* To think about how they can move

Resources
* Set of large footprints
* Paint
* Towels
* Long piece of wallpaper
* Shoes and boots (variety of sizes and types, including from other cultures, eg clog, ski boot, sandle)
* Card cut into shoe shapes
* Laces
* Plaster-impregnated bandage
* *The Mice Who Lived in the Shoe* by Rodney Peppe (Kestrel)

Activities
* Arrange a set of large footprints going across the floor, up the wall and over the ceiling before the children arrive. Ask them who they think has visited the room in the night and what they did.

* Let them take off their shoes and socks, dip their feet in paint and walk, run, skip, etc along a long piece of wallpaper and look at the marks that they have made. Use the paper as backing for a display.

* Draw round a shoe and cut out the shape. Ask the children to stand barefooted on the shape to see if the shoe would fit. Would the toes have room to wriggle?

* Use card shoe shapes for children to practise threading laces and tying bows.

* Have a shoe shop in the class room. Put shoes in order of size. Sort into sets using colours, fastenings, etc.

* Provide different shoes and make up stories about who they belong to, eg a (Cinderella) dance shoe, football boot, wellington, swimming fin. Include shoes and boots from other cultures.

Extensions/variations
* Make slippers by wrapping feet in plaster-impregnated bandage.

* Read *The Mice Who Lived in the Shoe*.

Assessment
* Is he/she able to place shoes in order of size?

Challenge
Who has the largest feet?

Growing up and getting bigger

Purpose
* To be aware of a sense of time and their own growth

Resources
* Baby clothes to grown-up wear
* Washing basket or suitcase
* Pictures and photographs
* Clothes line and pegs
* Paper
* Spinner or dice
* Photographs of children
* Clothes catalogues

Activities
* Bring in a washing basket or suitcase of clothes, eg a set of jumpers from birth to adult size. Can they find the one that would fit them? Relate the garments to different times in their lives. Peg then on a washing line in order of size.

* Make a game with cut-out paper shapes of trousers, jumpers, T-shirts and coats in different colours and sizes. Use a spinner or dice for the children to collect a set.

* Match the garments to photographs and children's drawings of events. Can they appreciate how fashion has changed?

* Can they decide which would be summer or winter wear? What reasons do they give?

Extension/variation
* Have a fashion parade. Cut out sets of clothes from catalogues.

Assessment
* Is he/she able to sequence a set of clothes from birth to the present day?

Challenge
Make a set of summer clothes.

Tea for two

Purpose
* To explore the different artefacts used for drinking and the materials that they are made from

Resources
* Cups, tumblers, babies' drinkers and bottles, paper cups, mugs, etc (not glass or thin china)
* Water tray
* Jugs and teapots
* Plastic bottles and cartons
* Plasticine, playdough and/or clay

Activities
* Begin with the rhyme 'Polly put the kettle on'. Talk about being careful with hot water.

* Use the water tray to find out which items will hold the most water, which is easy to pour and to fill and is easy to hold.

* Have a tea party in the home corner. How many cups of water will a teapot hold? Which is the best jug for pouring water? Which is the best drinker for a toddler?

Extension/variation
* Make Plasticine, playdough and clay pots. Which holds water? Which stays soft and which dries hard? Which can be painted?

Assessment
* Is he/she able to choose the container that will hold the most water?

 Challenge
Which is the best jug for pouring water?

Party plates

Purpose
* To explore the range of materials and sizes of plates
* To learn the technique of making and using papier mâché
* To extend their vocabulary on shape and size

Resources
* Storybook: *The Tiger Who Came to Tea* by Judith Kerr (Picture Lions)
* Plates of different sizes and materials, eg plastic, tin, pyrex, paper, ceramic, wood
* Printing materials
* Threading beads
* Oil
* Newsprint and white paper
* Glue
* Scissors
* Paint
* Varnish (for adult use)

Activities
* Read *The Tiger Who Came to Tea*. Provide a selection of plates of various sizes and ask which they would use for different occasions.

* Challenge the children to decorate paper plates by printing, eg using only two colours and two shapes, one colour and three shapes, etc. Can they make a pattern? Practise with threading beads first, then copy the pattern around the rim of the plate.

* Make papier mâché with the children. Slightly oil the surface of a plate and add a layer of newsprint paper pieces and glue. When it is dry add a second layer of plain white paper pieces and glue. When this is dry, trim around the edges before prising the paper plate away from the original. Let the children paint their plates and decorate them. Show the children canal boat designs, Clarice Cliff and other types of designs before they make their own. Varnish the plates for the children in order to preserve them.

Extension/variation
* Talk about the Greek tradition of smashing plates.

Assessment
* Is he/she able to use papier mâché successfully?

Challenge
Can you make a plate?

Mechanics at work

Purpose
✳ To raise awareness of the variety of materials used on their big toys, and why

Resources
✳ Large construction kits
✳ Big toys, including bicycles
✳ Workshop or garage role-play area
✳ Overalls and tools (eg spanners, clamps, screwdrivers, etc)

Activities
✳ Use large construction kits to make models, eg pram, car, scooter. Use the large toys, including bicycles.

✳ Have a garage area for role play.

✳ Place a tricycle or peddle car on a low table. In a small group look at all the moving parts. Name them and talk about how they work, eg rubber tyres, cushioned seat, steel frame, plastic bodywork. Give them time to explore how the peddles move the wheels. Can they make a model with a construction kit? How does it stop?

Extensions/variations
✳ Have a road system to peddle round and teach the rules of road safety.

✳ Make models using clamps, spanners and screwdrivers correctly.

Assessment
✳ Can he/she create a vehicle with wheels?

 Challenge
Do you know how to turn the wheels?

Time out

Purpose
✳ To plan an outing for a teddy bears' picnic, using all their previous knowledge about materials in order to make choices about suitable clothes to wear and what utensils to take

Resources
✳ Dressing-up clothes for children and toys
✳ Picnic equipment

Activities
✳ Plan an outing for the teddies and dolls, to have a picnic.

✳ Ask the children to decide what food and utensils they will need. How are they going to transport the picnic and the toys to the chosen site? Let the children make decisions on what they should wear, including on their heads and feet.

✳ Ask them to put a picnic basket together, including plates, cups and cutlery. Make sure that there is a set for each participant.

Assessment
Y Is he/she able to plan for a future event?

B Is he/she aware and interested in exploring differences in ideas and suggestions?

G Can he/she participate in the planning with reasoned ideas?

ELG Does he/she choose and use the apparatus with care and understanding? Is he/she able to take responsibility for part of the operation and participate in it fully?

Challenge
What do you need for a teddy bears' picnic?

Adding colours

Purpose

✳ To allow children time to explore and experiment with the effects of different colouring materials

Resources

✳ Wide range of art tools and materials

Activities

✳ Introduce one medium at a time and teach the skills of how to use the tools to create effects. Allow time for children to learn new techniques and to experiment for themselves. Give time for them to return to the table to practise.

✳ Provide large trays with a layer of thick liquid paint and use fingers, hands, forks, combs, sponges and various brushes to make patterns. Lay paper over the pattern to print off the effect for each child.

✳ Provide objects with an interesting shape or texture for printing. Try crumpled newspaper, sponges, potato shapes and bricks.

✳ Make print pictures and patterns.

Assessment

✳ Is he/she able to use paints to create a pattern?

 Challenge
Can you write your name in the paint?

Changing colours

Purpose
* To gain the skills of mixing colours and express their feelings through art
* To develop an aesthetic awareness of colour

Resources
* Thick and thin liquid paint
* Range of colouring materials (paint, chalk, pastel, crayon, dye, etc)
* Paper and card of different shapes, sizes and textures
* Chalkboard
* Draw program on computer
* Handkerchiefs, pillowcases or T-shirts
* Easels

Activities
* Have pots of thick liquid paint for children to pour and mix on trays. Talk about the colours they start with and the ones they make.

* Add colour to paper, chalkboards, card – use paint, chalk, pastel, crayon, dye, etc. Introduce one new item each week.

* Use the draw program on the computer for drawing and filling in colour.

* Use papers and card of different shapes, sizes and textures. Use flat surfaces and easels.

Extension/variation
* Use crayon dyes to make pictures on handkerchiefs, pillowcases and T-shirts. Make as presents for Mother's/Father's Day gifts.

Assessment
* Is he/she able to create a new colour by mixing?

Challenge
Can you make the paint change colour?

Bottled colours

Purpose
∗ To provide the stimuli for children to explore how liquids behave

Resources
∗ Plastic bottles of different shapes, sizes and colours, some with lids
∗ Water coloured with food colouring
∗ Coloured oil
∗ Sequins and/or glitter
∗ Washing-up liquid
∗ Straws
∗ Paper

Activities
∗ Add coloured liquid to plastic bottles of different shapes and sizes until they are quarter-, half-, three-quarters full, or full. Allow the children time to explore what happens when they move the bottle on its side or tip it upside down.

∗ Can they see through the coloured liquid? Try adding coloured oil, sequins or glitter.

∗ Make bubbles. Add a little washing-up liquid and shake the bottles with the top on.

∗ Provide bubble tubs and soapy liquid to create bubbles.

∗ Make bubble prints. Blow into the liquid through a straw and burst the bubbles onto paper.

Safety
∗ Watch that any liquid does not go in their eyes or their mouths (when blowing bubbles).

Assessment
∗ Is he/she able to blow bubbles?

 Challenge
Who can make the biggest bubble?

Moving colours

Purpose
✳ To help children appreciate beauty through pattern and colour

Resources
✳ Marbles
✳ Spinners
✳ Kaleidoscope
✳ Tops
✳ Luminous disco twirlers
✳ Flags
✳ Card or ply discs
✳ Dowel
✳ String

Activities
✳ Allow time for children to explore what happens to the colours and how the colours change when there is movement.

✳ Make spinners and tops using card or ply discs and dowel or string.

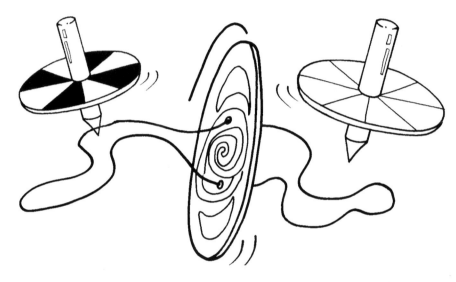

Assessment
✳ Does he/she observe changes in colour?

Challenge
What colours can you see when the toys move quickly?

Looking through colour

Purpose
✳ To allow children to discover that they can change images and create effects for themselves

Resources
✳ Cellophanes and acetates
✳ Bubblewrap
✳ Tissue paper
✳ Wrapping paper including foils
✳ Net
✳ Sunglasses, masks, sun visors, goggles, etc
✳ Tubes of varying lengths and diameters
✳ Rubber bands

Activities
✳ Cover windows with materials to create effects. Does the view change colour? Is the image still clear? Can the children see through the material?

✳ Have a collection of sunglasses, masks, sun visors and goggles for them to wear.

✳ Make spy tubes by covering the end of cylinders of different lengths and diameters. Show them how to fasten coloured cellophane over the end with a rubber band.

Assessment
✳ Is he/she able to discuss what they can see through transparent, translucent and opaque materials?

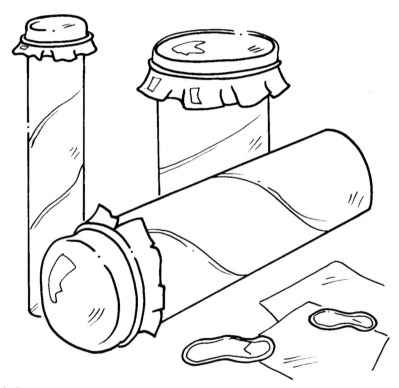

 Challenge
Can you make a new colour with pieces of cellophane?

Light and fire

Purpose
✳ To deepen knowledge of cultures and beliefs by discussing Divali and candles used as religious symbols

Resources
✳ Collection of candle holders
✳ Candles
✳ Birthday cake
✳ Reference books

Activities
✳ Light candles for someone's birthday or light a candle at prayer time. Spend some time looking at the flame. Discuss the amount of light, the smell, the changes taking place, safety and fire.

✳ Create a display of candles and candle holders and explain the significance of candles as part of religions around the world.

✳ Visit a church and see the candles. Alternatively, invite someone to come and talk about Divali and show Divali candles.

✳ Ask the children to close their eyes while a scented candle is burning. Can they say when they first smell the scent? Can they describe the smell?

Extension/variation
✳ Extend the discussion to bonfires and Halloween pumpkins if appropriate.

Safety
✳ Raise awareness of the dangers of candles and fire. If using candles, use nightlights where possible. Always place candles on a bed of sand on a metal tray and take care. Do not allow children to lean over a candle.

Assessment
✳ Does he/she know that lit candles provide light?

Challenge
Does a candle have a smell?

Light and dark

Purpose
* To realize that the absence of light is dark, and without light there is no colour

Resources
* Torches
* Large dark box or covered-over area (eg thick curtain placed over a table)
* Coloured objects

Activities
* Cover a table with thick curtains to create a den, or use a very large cardboard box. Provide torches for children to use in the dark. Allow time for them to feel safe and comfortable with being in the dark.

* Ask them what they can see with very little or no light. Provide a set of coloured objects. Which colour can they identify first? Which is hardest to see? Can they see shapes? Are they able to identify objects? Can they guess what objects are by the feel, sound and smell of them?

* Make guessing games and record their answers on a chart.

Assessment
* Does he/she know that they cannot see when it is dark?

 Challenge
Can you see things in the dark?

Shining, luminous and dull

Purpose
* To extend their knowledge about materials and the world around them

Resources
* Collection of items: some smooth and polished (plastic mirrors, marbles and Christmas tree baubles); others dull and rough
* black paper
* pins (for practitioner to prick holes in paper)
* luminous objects, eg stars, pictures on T-shirts and other clothes, stickers, etc

Activities
* Talk about night time and the night sky. Say 'Twinkle, twinkle, little star' together.

* Talk about the sun and the moon, eg when we see them. Ask the children to look for the moon and to draw the shape. Have they noticed the changing shape, and the sequence? Make a moon chart.

* Discuss the dangers of looking at the sun.

* Ask them what they think the stars are, and how far away they are. Make pin pricks in black paper in patterns the same as the common constellations. Fasten these on the window so that the light shines through.

* Provide a collection of luminous objects, eg stars. Place these in the dark corner.

* Do the children have pyjamas or T-shirts with luminous pictures on?

* Have a dressing-up session for children to wear luminous clothing such as police jackets, patrol crossing coat, strips on anoraks and schoolwear.

* Have a fashion parade with the lights very low. Discuss the reasons for wearing luminous clothes and reinforce the dangers of night-time traffic and the importance of being seen in the dark.

Assessment
* Does he/she know the difference between shining, luminous and dull?

Challenge
Find something that you can see in the dark.

Mirror, mirror, on the wall

Purpose
✳ To encourage children to observe and to spend more time looking carefully at things

Resources
✳ Dressing-up mirrors and make-up mirrors
✳ Dressing-up clothes
✳ Make up and/or face paints
✳ Mirror card and sheet
✳ Plastic mirrors
✳ Concave and convex mirrors
✳ Reflective surfaces, eg shiny metal tins, Christmas baubles
✳ Mirror puzzle books, eg *'M' is for Mirror* by Duncan Birmingham (Tarquin)

Activities
✳ Make a fairground wobbly mirror with a large sheet of reflective material. Provide flexible plastic mirrors for children to manipulate and change the image seen.

✳ Use large dress mirrors with the dressing-up box. Have make-up mirrors to look at. Ask them to make funny faces, sad and happy, etc. Experiment with make up and face paints.

✳ Ask the children to dance in front of a mirror and to watch their movements.

✳ Look at the reflections and images in some surfaces. Talk about the shape, size and position of the images. Can the children see themselves in all of the surfaces?

✳ Look at reflections of objects in shiny surfaces, including Christmas baubles. Ask questions: Is the shape the same? Is the colour the same? Is the image the same way round, right way up, same size, etc?

Extensions/variations
✳ Use mirror puzzle books or picture cards with small plastic mirrors to alter the pictures.

✳ Make a hall of mirrors with sheets of plastic mirror or tin foil.

Safety
✳ Cover glass mirrors with clear sticky-back plastic to make them safer for children to use. Take care with glass mirrors and reflecting light in eyes.

Assessment
✳ Does he/she use mirrors well to observe him/herself?

Challenge
Can you make a thin toy look fatter with a mirror?

Elmer the elephant

Purpose
✳ To develop the skill of discrimination and raise awareness of colour matching
✳ To learn the names of colours

Resources
✳ Storybook: *Elmer* by David McKee (Red Fox)
✳ Paint charts
✳ Materials

Activities
✳ Read the story of *Elmer*, the patchwork elephant.

✳ Make a large picture of Elmer and ask the children to match the colours with other pieces of material. Can they make their own Elmer?

✳ Rainbow paints. Extend the activity out of doors. Cut out small squares of colour from paint charts. Give these out to the children and ask them to find something (a flower, leaf, twig, pebble, etc) the same colour as the rainbow paint pieces.

Assessment
Y   Can he/she explore and maintain an interest in the activity?

B   Is he/she able to make choices as to the colour and materials to use?

G   Is he/she able to discuss if he/she is pleased with the result?

ELG Is he/she able to make aesthetic judgements for him/herself? Does he/she compliment other children on their finished work?

 Challenge
Can you match Elmer's colours?

Sounds and rhythm

Purpose
✳ To recognize and explore how sounds can be made and changed

Resources
✳ Drum
✳ Beaters
✳ Piano

Activities
✳ Listen to a single drum beat. Ask the children to watch the movements, and listen to the sounds of the drum.

✳ Use different beaters.

✳ Sing 'Peter hammers with one hammer' as an action rhyme.

✳ Play notes on the piano and ask the children to strike the same notes.

Assessment
✳ Can he/she copy a sound?

Challenge
Can you copy the drum sounds?

Fast and slow, loud and soft

Purpose
✳ To recognize a range of sounds

Resources
✳ Clocks
✳ Beaters
✳ Drums
✳ Piano
✳ Triangle and other percussion instruments

Activities
✳ Listen to the sounds made by different clocks.

✳ Use the action rhyme 'Tick tock goes my daddy's big clock' to encourage children to move in time to the beat, using drums and beaters.

✳ Show the children how a piano is played – keys and pedals, loud and soft, high and low.

Assessment
✳ Is he/she able to create the sound of a clock using a musical instrument?

Challenge
Which clock can you hear?

Bangers

Purpose
* To make their own banging and tapping instruments

Resources
* Triangle
* Drums
* Range of beaters
* Pots, pans, boxes, tins, etc

Activities
* Allow time for children to explore the sounds which percussion instruments make. Provide a range of beaters.

* Challenge them to find something that makes an interesting sound.

Assessment
* Is he/she able to make their own percussion instrument?

Challenge
Can you tap your name?

Shaking sounds

Purpose
* To observe that materials can make a variety of sounds

Resources
* Maracas
* Rainmakers
* Plastic and metal pots with lids
* Rice, stones, dried peas, gravel, buttons, counters
* Sticky tape

Activities
* Show the children a rainmaker and use it with the action rhyme 'I hear thunder'. Let the children play with the maracas.

* Ask the children to make their own shaker. Can they guess what is inside their friend's shaker?

Assessment
* Can he/she tell you how his/her own shaker was made?

Challenge
Guess what is inside the shaking pot.

Twanging sounds

Purpose
* To extend their experiences of sounds

Resources
* Guitar
* Violin
* Elastic bands
* Boxes (range of sizes)

Activities
* Demonstrate the different way that sounds are made using string instruments. Talk about high and low sounds.

* Provide a selection of elastic bands and boxes for children to make their own 'twangers'.

* Use open and closed boxes and tins for a variety of sounds.

Extension/variation
* Show a video of a rock band.

Safety
* Be careful about elastic bands snapping.

Assessment
* Is he/she able to create high and low sounds?

 ## Challenge
Can you make a high note twanger?

Blowing sounds

Purpose
* To experience wind instruments

Resources
* Balloons
* Toy trumpets
* Party blowers
* Recorder
* Pan pipes
* Penny whistle
* Mouth organ
* Paper straws

Activities
* Ask the children to let the air out of a balloon to make a squeak.

* Look at a range of wind instruments and explore how they are played.

* Cut a 'v' in the end of a paper straw. The straw should make a noise when blown. Use straws of different lengths to vary the sound. Place the 'v' in the mouth and blow gently to create a sound.

Extension/variation
* Make a pin hole in the straw and use as a simple recorder, covering and uncovering the hole.

Safety
* If things are put in mouths they need to be disinfected after each child has finished.

Assessment
* Does he/she understand that sounds can be made by blowing air?

Challenge
Can you make a noise by blowing?

Noises we make

Purpose
* To appreciate the sounds that living things can make

Resources
* Tape-recording, video or CD-Rom of animal sounds

Activities
* Ask the children to make their own noises – hum, talk, sing, clap, etc. Tell a story and encourage them to make the appropriate sound effects.

* Talk about the sounds that animals make. Listen to the tape recording, video or CD-Rom of animal sounds. Can they imitate the sounds?

Extension/variation
* Use sound-matching games.

Assessment
* Can he/she make appropriate noises to accompany a story?

Challenge
Can you sound like an animal?

Sounds we like

Purpose
* To recognize sound patterns and match movements to music

Resources
* Musical boxes and spinning tops
* Radio, tape-recorder, TV
* Music program on a computer

Activities
* Listen to, move to and talk about sounds that the children like.

* Can they use a music program on the computer to create a tune?

* Invent movements to a range of sounds.

* Can they use a tape-recorder, or participate in TV or radio programmes, singing along with the presenters?

Assessment
* Does he/she respond rhythmically to sounds?

Challenge
Make up a dance to a piece of music.

Warning sounds

Purpose
* To raise awareness of sounds around us, indoors and out

Resources
* Real and toy phones
* Interactive reading program for computer
* Bells and alarms
* Toy fire engines, police cars and ambulances
* Hoods (or ear muffs), hats, caps

Activities
* Can they use a phone, or role play using a mobile phone?

* Say 'I hear thunder'. Can they make a noise like thunder? How far away can they hear it?

* Introduce the interactive reading program on the computer. Listen for the bell sound indicating they should move to the next page.

* Traffic sounds – staying safe. Can they hear as well if they have a hood, hat or cap (or ear muffs) over their ears?

Extension/variation
* Have a road safety session about crossing the road.

Assessment
* Is he/she able to give examples of warning sounds?

 Challenge
Can you use the phone?

Everyday sounds

Purpose
* To raise awareness of everyday sounds

Resources
* Tick sheet for children to record sounds heard in neighbourhood
* Pictures and taped sounds
* Variety of objects that make sounds
* Blindfold

Activities
* Go for a 'sound' walk around the building. Stop and listen to the different sounds.

* Go for a 'sound walk' in the neighbourhood. Provide a picture tick sheet, for children to record when they have heard a sound. Discuss the sounds when back in school.

* In groups, play sound games, where children have to match pictures to sounds they can hear on a tape.

* Tell a story involving lots of sounds. Give each child a different object to make a sound when it is mentioned in the story.

* Play a listening game. Place objects related to sounds on a table or in a ring, eg alarm clock, squeaky toy, rattle, whistle, bell, musical instruments. Blindfold a child and ask them to listen to a sound. Remove the blindfold and ask the child to identify the source.

Assessment
Y   Does he/she show interest by listening and wanting to make a sound?
B   Can he/she identify sounds?
G   Is he/she able to recreate a sound?
ELG Is he/she able to listen to sounds, and respond through movement, identification or by recreating the sound?

Challenge
Can you make the sounds to go with a story?

Moving things

Purpose
✳ To raise awareness that things are moving in their world

Resources
✳ A video of the seaside, traffic, a busy street, etc
✳ Paper
✳ Crayons

Activities
✳ Watch the video and discuss everything that is moving.

✳ Look outside or sit outside and look for things that move, eg trees, clouds, birds, washing, people, traffic. Make a picture chart of things that move.

✳ Use toy cars and building bricks to make a model street.

Assessment
✳ Is he/she able to identify still and moving objects?

Challenge
Can you see five moving things?

What can the wind do?

Purpose
✳ To realize that the wind cannot be seen, but the effect can be seen and felt

Resources
✳ Windmills
✳ Flags and streamers
✳ Large sheets of card
✳ Bubbles
✳ Materials to make paper streamers and flags

Activities
✳ Go outside on a windy day with a selection of resources. Allow time for children to feel and see the effect of the wind. Use the correct vocabulary for a range of wind strengths.

✳ Provide large sheets of card for the children to hold to feel the force.

✳ Blow bubbles and watch them sail away.

✳ Provide materials to make paper streamers and flags.

Assessment
✳ Does he/she understand that air cannot be seen but its effects can?

Challenge
Make a streamer that will work in a breeze.

Mechanical toys

Purpose
* To explore the different mechanisms used to make toys move

Resources
* Range of toys, large and small
* Construction kits

Activities
* Let the children play with the toys and see how they move. Ask them to pick one and show you how to make it work. Look at how the toys move.

* Put the toys into sets, depending on how they work: push-and-pull, mechanical, gravity, electrical, etc.

Assessment
* Can he/she discuss the mechanism in a toy?

Challenge
Make a toy.

Moving things

Purpose
* To experience the forces of pull and push

Resources
* *Moving Molly* by Shirley Hughes (Red Fox)
* Large boxes
* Rollers
* Large toys
* Removable sticky labels
* Construction kits

Activities
* Read *Moving Molly*.

* Place a large box in the doorway and ask the children to help you move it across the room. Ask the children to stick 'push' or 'pull' removable sticky labels on all the big toys and around the room on doors, drawers, etc.

* Make trolleys and carts with construction kits.

Assessment
* Does he/she understand the words *push* and *pull*?

Challenge
Find a toy to push or pull.

See-saw, Marjorie Daw

Purpose
To explore balance

Resources
✳ Playground toys, construction and recycled materials

Activities
✳ Begin with the rhyme 'See-saw, Marjorie Daw' and ask the children to make a see-saw.

✳ Who will sit on the other end to make it balance? Provide tubes, cans and flat lengths of strong materials.

✳ Make a mobile using coat hangers and fasten objects or pictures to it. Draw pictures to hang on it.

Assessment
✳ Can he/she make a see-saw that will balance?

Challenge
Make a see-saw to sit on with a friend.

People on the bus

Purpose
* To act out a series of movements
* To cooperate in a group situation

Resources
* Cardboard boxes
* Card and sheets of flexible plastic
* Paint
* Chairs or benches
* Hat and bag
* Paper plates

Activities
* Sing together the song 'The wheels on the bus'. Design and make a bus with the children, large enough for the children to sit in. Ask for suggestions as to what they want on it, eg number plate, lights, door, etc. Let them paint the bus. Add chairs or benches to sit in it.

* Have a rota for the bus driver and create a uniform. Have a bag and tickets.

* Add moving parts, eg wheels, door, steering wheel and gear stick.

* Give time for groups of children to go for bus trips.

* Make a large frieze using paper plates for each child to decorate to make their own heads to go in the bus windows.

Assessment
* Is he/she able to describe a sequence of movements in the correct order?

 Challenge
Draw a picture to show how you made the bus.

Magnets

Purpose
* To explore the properties of magnets

Resources
* Collection of magnets of all shapes
* Magnetic and non-magnetic items
* Magnetic games and fridge magnets
* Magnetic wands and marbles
* Flat magnetic sheet
* Fishing games

Activities
* Allow time for the children to discover the force of magnetism. They can find things that a magnet will pick up, things that a magnet won't pick up, and things that are partly magnetic.

* Encourage them to explore the strength of a magnet by how many paper clips it can lift.

* They can investigate which materials a magnet can work through.

* Let the children experience the 'push' and 'pull' of one magnet with another.

Safety
* Warn the children not to take a magnet near any computers or near a watch.

Assessment
* Is he/she able to use a magnet correctly?

 Challenge
Which is the strongest magnet?

Pop-up cards - how do they work?

Purpose
✳ To construct with a purpose in mind, using scissors, glue, card and a variety of materials for decoration

Resources
✳ A variety of bought pop-up cards
✳ Pop-up books
✳ Paper plates
✳ Scissors, etc

Activities
✳ Share a pop-up book with the children. Show them all of the mechanisms.

✳ Provide some pop-up cards or structures that you have made for the children to examine.

✳ Help them to create a card with some form of movement, eg a pop-up picture coming up through a slit, a picture on a folded paper spring, or a rocking card made by folding a paper plate in half.

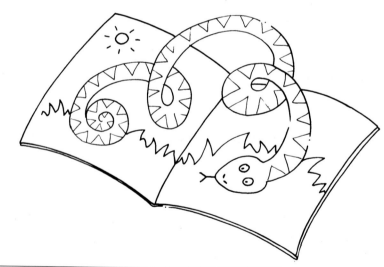

Assessment
✳ Can he/she create movement using card?

Challenge
Can you make a special card with a moving part?

PE movement

Purpose
✳ For children to explore and appreciate the different movements that they can make

Resources
✳ Small PE apparatus
✳ Pipe cleaners

Activities
✳ Ask the children to move only one tiny part of themselves, eg a little finger, then to slowly increase the movement throughout the body until they are shaking all over.

✳ Reverse the process until they are only moving a different part.

✳ Ask them to make faces and observe a partner.

✳ Play 'Simon says'.

✳ Provide small apparatus, hoops, bats, balls, quoits, bean bags, etc, and give time for children to practise using them. Teach the skills of throwing and catching.

✳ Ask the children to work in twos and to move a piece of apparatus between them in as many ways as possible. Can they name the force they used, eg *push*, *throw*, *kick*, *hit*?

Extension/variation
✳ Use pipe cleaners to make model figures to stick on a class picture of a PE lesson.

Assessment
✳ Does he/she have good control over large and small body movements?

✴ Challenge
How many ways can you move a ball?

Play time

Purpose

✳ To explore all forms of movement using the playground apparatus

Resources

✳ Outdoor equipment
✳ Ramps
✳ Boxes
✳ Toys, etc
✳ *It's Polar* by Elaine Moss (André Deutsch)

Activities

✳ Encourage the children to think about how they are moving. Introduce suitable vocabulary, ie *force*, *push*, *pull*, *balance*, *swing*, *turn*, etc.

✳ Make an assault course for their teddy bears, or for the children to attempt.

✳ Create ramps and slopes for them to go up and down.

✳ Read *It's Polar* and try sliding boxes down a ramp. Use a ramp for sending toy vehicles down. How far do they travel? Which is the best? What happens if they raise the ramp?

Assessment

Y   Can he/she move and stop on request?
B   Can he/she negotiate a way across apparatus?
G   Can he/she describe his/her movements with appropriate vocabulary?
ELG Is he/she able to create movement by using the appropriate apparatus?

Challenge

Make an assault course for Teddy.

Things that use electricity

Purpose
* To raise awareness of electricity and its dangers

Resources
* Collection of electrical appliances
* Pictures of electrical appliances
* Stickers
* Catalogues
* Tape-recorder, radio, telephone

Activities
* Have some examples of electrical goods, eg hair dryer, electric and mechinical tin openers, electric and battery-powered clocks, radio, tape-recorder, electric and non-electric kettles, electric iron and flat-iron. Ask why some won't work and which need to be plugged into the electric socket. Talk about battery power, mechanical power and electricity.

* Discuss what happened before all the gadgets were invented.

* Ask the children to name things in the classroom that need electricity. They could put stickers on the things they find.

* Provide catalogues for them to cut out pictures of things at home that need electricity.

* Let them use the tape-recorder, radio and telephone.

Safety
* Emphasize the dangers of electricity.

Assessment
* Does he/she understand the dangers of electricity?

Challenge
Put a sticker on something that uses electricity.

Using the computer

Purpose

✳ To raise awareness of the safe use of computers

Resources

✳ Computer
✳ Draw program
✳ Word-processing program

Activities

✳ Talk to the children and find out how much they know and understand about computers. Make sure that they know the rules about safety and are aware of the electricity being used.

✳ Use programs appropriate to their needs: talking books, number games, draw program, interactive games.

Assessment

✳ Can he/she use the computer confidently?

Challenge

Can you write your name using the keyboard?

Toys with batteries

Purpose
* To develop an understanding of battery power

Resources
* Battery-powered toys, clockwork toys
* Large programmable toy, such as Roamer

Activities
* Let the children play with the toys. Question them as to what makes the toys work. Are they able to appreciate when the power is low and why the toy will not function. Compare toys that have new batteries with ones that have used batteries.

* Make one set of battery-powered toys and another of clockwork toys. Open a toy and show the children the battery inside. Will the toy work if the battery is removed?

* Introduce a large programmable toy such as Roamer.

Assessment
* Does he/she understand that a battery is a power source?

Challenge
Can you switch the toy on and off?

Torches

Purpose
* To extend their understanding of battery power

Resources
* A selection of torches and batteries
* Table covered with thick cloth

Activities
* Have a selection of torches, some with no batteries, some with new and others with used batteries. Ask the children to find the best torch. Can they put them in sets? Why won't some light at all? Show them inside the torch. Discuss why some are dull and some bright.

* Cover a table with a thick cloth for the children to sit under in order to try out the torches.

Safety
Never use rechargeable batteries, or cut a battery open.

Assessment
* Does he/she know that there are a range of batteries with different amounts of power?

Challenge
Can you match the battery to the torch?

Shadows

Purpose
* To appreciate that light makes shadows

Resources
* Bright torches
* Overhead projector
* Slide projector
* Whiteboard or piece of paper
* Small objects
* Black paper
* Scissors
* Bright torches

Activities
* Darken the room and use a beam of light from a projector to create shadows. Let the children make shadow shapes on the wall, whiteboard or piece of paper.

* Place objects in the light beam. Can the children guess what they are from the shadow?

* On black paper draw round shadows made by objects and cut out the shapes. Can the children match the shapes to the objects?

* Cut out shapes of objects, numbers and letters. Can the children identify the object, number or letter from the shadow?

* Give children bright torches and see if they can make shadows that will grow and change shape by moving the torch about.

Assessment
* Can he/she create a shadow?

Challenge
Can you make a shadow dance?

Making a simple circuit

Purpose
✳ To introduce children to electrical components and make a simple circuit

Resources
✳ Batteries of 4.5 volts or less
✳ Bulbs with a matching voltage rating
✳ Wire with crocodile clips on the ends

Activities
✳ Show the children how to use the crocodile clips. Allow them time to explore how to join the components and make the light bulb work.

✳ Show them where the connections are on the battery, the bulb, and the wires. Emphasize that each needs two connections.

Assessment
✳ Can he/she make a simple circuit?

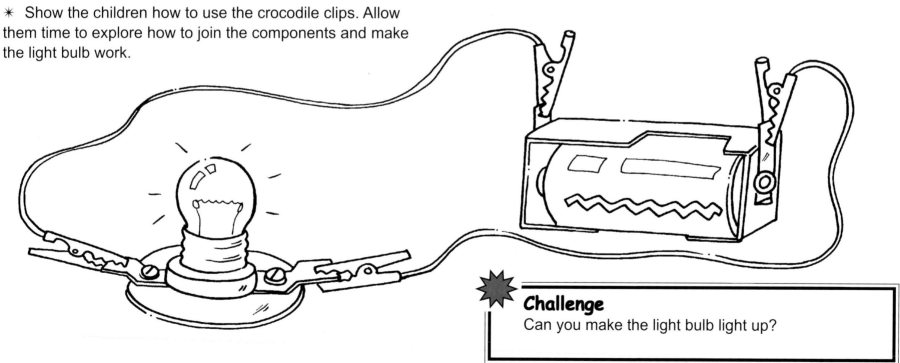

Challenge
Can you make the light bulb light up?

One wire or two?

Purpose
✳ To extend children's understanding of how to make a circuit

Resources
✳ Batteries of 4.5 volts or less
✳ Bulbs with a matching voltage rating
✳ Wire with crocodile clips on the ends
✳ Clip-on or screw bulb holders

Activities
✳ Work with the children to explore how many different ways they can connect the components and make the bulb light. Try placing the bulb on one battery connection, and placing a connecting wire from the bulb to the other battery connection.

✳ Show the children how to connect two wires to a bulb holder and make a circuit.

Assessment
✳ Can he/she make a bulb light?

Challenge
How many ways can you make a circuit?

What is a switch?

Purpose
✳ To appreciate that a break in the circuit is a simple switch

Resources
✳ Batteries of 4.5 volts or less
✳ Bulbs with a matching voltage rating
✳ Wire with crocodile clips on the ends
✳ Screw or clip-on bulb holders
✳ Screwdrivers

Activity
✳ Give children time to experiment and make a simple circuit with a light bulb. Ask them to find a way to turn the light off. Children may simply move a wire, disconnect a crocodile clip, or unscrew the light bulb.

Assessment
✳ Can he/she switch a light on and off?

Challenge
Can you switch your light on and off?

Static electricity

Purpose
✳ To find out about static electricity

Resources
✳ Balloons
✳ Woollen or silk fabrics
✳ Tissue paper
✳ Plastic rulers
✳ Confetti
✳ Shoe boxes
✳ Clingfilm

Activities
✳ Use blown-up balloons. Ask the children to rub them on their clothes or pieces of woollen or silk fabrics.

✳ Tie the balloons with string. What happens if two balloons are held by the string? Can they feel a force pushing or pulling if they hold two balloons close together?

✳ Hold a rubbed balloon against a wall, then let go. Hold one against someone's hair, or over a pile of tissue paper pieces. Give the children time to try out all of the suggestions.

✳ Try rubbing a plastic ruler and holding it over confetti.

✳ Make small tissue paper butterflies and place in a shoe box. Cover the top with clingfilm. Rub the clingfilm and watch the butterflies fly.

Assessment
✳ Does he/she understand that static is a form of electricity?

Challenge
Can you make your friend's hair stand on end?

Decorative lights

Purpose
* To appreciate the uses of electricity

Resources
* Fairy lights
* Lamps and lanterns

Activities
* To enhance the room and make an attractive display, use sets of fairy lights and lamps. Discuss what makes the lights work, the safety aspects, and ask the children to talk about their Christmas lights and decorations.

* Can they paint or draw a picture matching the colours of the lights?

Safety
* All electrical appliances must be tested each year.

Assessment
Y   Does he/she show an interest and participate in the activities?

B   Does he/she know how to switch equipment on and off?

G   Is he/she able to perform simple functions using ICT equipment?

ELG Is he/she able to talk about the use of ICT and to use electrical components safely and confidently?

Challenge
Make a pattern of colours for the lights.